W9-BNE-882

CHILDREN WITH SUBTLE PERCEPTUAL-MOTOR DIFFICULTIES

JOHN E. CRAWFORD

Clinical Psychologist in Education
Formerly Supervisor of Special Education
Lawrence and Venango Counties, Pennsylvania

BRIAR CLIFF COLLEGE
LIBRARY
SIOUX CITY, IOWA

STANWIX HOUSE, INC.
Pittsburgh

Copyright 1966 by Stanwix House, Inc.
Printed in the United States of America.

All rights reserved. No part of this book may be used
or reproduced in any manner whatsoever without written permission except in the case of brief quotations
embodied in critical articles and reviews. For information address Stanwix House, Inc., 3020 Chartiers Ave-
nue, Pittsburgh, Pennsylvania 15204.

Published simultaneously in Canada by
J. M. Dent & Sons (Canada) Ltd.
Toronto, Ontario

LC
4580
.C72

Library of Congress Catalog Card Number:
66—19434

FOREWORD

Good teachers have always wanted to know more about the causes of learning disability and distress in children. Clearer understanding of the causes of such trouble can open ways for interested teachers to invent effective remedial methods and materials for these children.

The old controversies that used to be mixed with great fervor about the psychic causes of school failure in many children have been giving way to better insight into organic as well as emotional factors in a large proportion of such cases. Better team-relationships have been developing in recent years in many school communities, between the classroom teacher, the school physician and nurse, the counselor and psychologist, the reading specialist, speech clinician, the parent, and even the child himself whenever possible, to try to discern the *full* causes of his trouble.

Children With Subtle Perceptual-Motor Difficulties is arriving on this encouraging scene at just the right moment to promote such cooperation toward understanding and helping such boys and girls. This book came out of the author's experience both as a classroom teacher and as school psychologist with such children. The paramount aim of the book is simply to help good teachers recognize perceptual-motor-expressive difficulties in a child early enough to offer the most gain from remedial techniques. Thoughtful teachers, counselors, principals, and parents who have wondered how to discern children with possible cerebral injury or dysfunction, from whatever cause, will find this book encouraging.

The chapters are sound neurologically, yet are written for clear understanding by persons who may not have studied much about the structure and function of the central nervous

iii

65396

system and the other intricately related and supporting organ-systems of the body.

Before we can do much to help a child who is lost in the woods, we have to get to where he is. *Children With Subtle Perceptual-Motor Difficulties* aims to help good teachers do just that for many youngsters.

It is an excellent book for browsing, as well as for careful study. The author's own warm hopefulness and practicality about all children have spilled over into the chapters to make them valuable in any school where boys and girls have learning trouble.

Luis Schut, M. D.
Neurosurgeon
University of Pennsylvania
Graduate Hospital

PREFACE

Every book has roots in the experiences of the author. The chapters of this book had their inceptions in the challenges that came to me during many busy years as the psychologist and supervisor of special education in Lawrence and Venango County schools, in western Pennsylvania. Major portions of each chapter were used in our in-service seminars for special class teachers. Basic concepts had to stand the test of classroom application, with real children.

Such experiences kept us all aware that children never are *just* children. No child can be completely dimensioned by test scores, physical measurements, or neuro-psychiatric indices. These measures still do not reveal the whole child, nor can they truly explain how he feels or why he behaves as he does at times. The essence of a child is not so easily discerned.

A new and healthy respect for this fact is evident in many professional fields recently. Some of the old tools and techniques for cataloging and resolving children's problems are beginning to appear less magical and less powerful than they once did. Psychology and education are showing a warmer sense of humility about many facets of the mind of a child that are not easy to comprehend. Life has been making us learn again that the most carefully worded diagnosis still has never created warm understanding or love—or a desire to do better. These things come oftener out of the wise heart than out of the erudite mind.

In this new soil, better understanding of all children is beginning to flourish again. Good teachers are realizing they can spot youngsters with special learning difficulties, and implement remedial methods that are effective with these boys and girls. This book has been aimed simply to promote these attitudes and skills among thoughtful teachers, particularly with children who show perceptual-motor-language troubles.

The chapters reflect my own increasing belief that many children have trudged along in school for years misjudged and mislabeled. It was easier to say that a child was "very retarded mentally" than to find out why he seemed so slow. Failing him was not as arduous as inventing ways to help him circumvent his handicap. Insisting that the teacher's job did not include such special insight and innovation took less time than studying books about teaching exceptional children. Transferring the child to some special class — perhaps in another building several miles away—was commonplace in many districts. At least this was a good move for some children who had had severe learning difficulties. For too many other girls and boys it was a poor move.

Good teachers have always sensed that few children are truly retarded, and fewer children *want* to fail in school. Good teachers have always been willing to look a little more closely at every boy and girl who is having school trouble. Such teachers probably will find this book helpful. It was written in this hope.

Across many of the pages still stride the children I have known intimately for years. Rickie, Ginger, Kathy, Ted, and a hundred others often come to mind, for these were the children who taught us two important facts of life:

How marvelously the brain can modify and at least partially restore itself to healthy functioning, after injury or damage. And how often this happens even when no one would have believed it could happen.

John E. Crawford

CHILDREN WITH SUBTLE PERCEPTUAL-MOTOR DIFFICULTIES

FOREWORD   iii
PREFACE   v
Chapter 1: THESE ARE OUR CHILDREN TOO 1
    Children have endurance limits 1
    Notes on a jittery youngster.. 4
    How some of these children have been described 5
    Broad syndrome in many of these boys and girls........ 10
Chapter 2: SOME DIFFERENTIALS ABOUT THESE
        CHILDREN 14
    Seeing all children in a more hopeful light 14
    The brain and CNS are remarkably self-restoring 16
    Some dangers to children at nativity 16
    Wide effects of minute brain injury 20
    Signs of the hyperactive child at home, school 20
    Impulsive and compulsive children 23
    Hyperactive children vs. slow developers 26
    There probably are few very slow developers 29
    Anxiety can tinge the clinical picture 31
    Interhemisphere confusion in many poor readers 31
    Reading disability—the Achilles' heel of many children 33
    These boys and girls live in every community 36
Chapter 3: THESE BOYS AND GIRLS ARE BEING
        HELPED 38
    More teachers are becoming interested 39

Physicians are taking more time to check 39
Fewer children are now being wrongly tagged 40
The EEG is coming into wider diagnostic use 43
Cortical irritability in many of these children 46
Their drawings sometimes reflect the deeper trouble...... 48
Some of these children seem schizophrenic too 51
Brain injury does not rule out hopeful prognosis 55
Careful diagnosis leads to better therapy 56
Chapter 4: THE BEST CATALYZER STILL IS A GOOD
    TEACHER.. 62
The new point of view about invisibly handicapped
    children 62
Children need to be ready to learn 65
The teacher's warmth and wisdom are factors too 66
Some newer texts that offer help to good teachers 66
Creative-minded teachers have a head start 70
Chapter 5: ALERT TEACHERS CAN DISCERN THE
    SIGNALS 72
Hopeful teachers are inclined to be more helpful 73
Some *clinical* tests teachers can adapt 73
General impression of the child 74
The child's health history 74
His school record may reveal deeper problems 76
Speech peculiarities 77
Number-concept signs... 78
Difficulties in copying 79
Reproducing designs from memory 79
Figure-ground difficulties 82
Difficulties in right-left orientation............................ 83
Finger differentiation 83
Body-midline identification 84
Subtle tactile disturbances 84
Difficulties with laterality 85
Flicker-frequency trouble 86
Vision difficulties 86
Hearing difficulties 88

The team approach to all these children 89
Chapter 6: EMOTIONAL CONFLICTS OFTEN CLOUD
    THE PICTURE 90
Many children suffer discouragement 90
Emotional stress can be very harmful........................... 91
Children need to feel valued 92
The surface signals in a child can vary 93
Jittery children need the right controls......................... 95
Understanding these children takes some wisdom 97
The kind of classroom atmosphere these children
    most need 98
Good teachers like to do these things for all children
    in their care 99
Chapter 7: MANY OF THESE CHILDREN HAVE
    GONE MISUNDERSTOOD SO LONG 101
Not all discouraged children are boys 101
Writing often reflects the trouble............................... 102
So do some *performance* tests 105
And figure reproduction tests 108
The signals sometimes are subclinical, but they can
    be discerned with care 110
Teachers have caused school trouble in some
    children, too 115
Cerebrally involved youngsters often become very
    cautious and sensitive 118
Calm classroom atmosphere is imperative 119
Chapter 8: ENDOCRINE DYSFUNCTIONS CAN
    UPSET SCHOOL ABILITY TOO 121
Swift advances are coming in the field of biochemistry .. 122
All the glands are intimately linked 123
Thyroid problems.. 123
Pituitary problems 126
Adrenal problems 128
Gonads: testicles and ovaries 129
Other glands: pancreas 130
Children go through metamorphosis too 131

Chapter 9: SOME CENTRAL NERVOUS SYSTEM
    DYSFUNCTIONS 133
  Intensive research is revealing the marvels
    of our brains and nervous systems........................... 134
  And something of their dysfunctions too 135
  Measles can damage 135
  So can other infections 138
  And vascular lesions 140
  And tumors 141
  So can physical injuries 142
  Developmental defects may leave many troubles 143
  As can degenerative diseases 143
  Diseases arising from some toxins 144
  Some metabolic diseases and dysbalances 145
  Demyelinating diseases 145
  Other diseases of as-yet-unknown etiology can still
    hurt a child's brain and nervous system 145
  Prognosis in any case is the province of the physician.. 146

Chapter 10: MOST FAMILY DOCTORS NOW CAN
SPOT CNS TROUBLE IN CHILDREN 151
  He has the special knowledge and the wide experience... 152
  He knows what to look for in the child 152
  Something of the examination procedure 153
  Testing the child's general mental functioning.............. 153
  Testing his cerebral functioning more specifically 154
  Testing his motor strength and reaction...................... 154
  Testing cranial nerve functions 155
  Looking for cerebellar trouble in the child................... 158
  Checking the motor nerve system 158
  Testing the sensory system 159
  Testing the child's reflex status 159

Chapter 11: OTHER CLINICAL FACETS OF THESE
    CHILDREN 161
  Girls and boys often have keener insight about
    themsleves than grownups have believed.................. 161
  We frequently underestimate our children 161

La bête noire: the residue of organicity 162

Parents' secret feelings can be very important................ 163

Any degree of damage can have wide effects in
the child 164

There are many reasons why these children behave
so immaturely at times 165

There often is an overlay of anxiety.............................. 167

And discouragement too 168

Every symptom in such a child may not be
organically based or caused 172

Association deficit pathology (ADP) is a better
term than schizophrenia 175

Adolescent signals of subtle ADP levels 176

Some of the etiology.. 178

Electrochemical bases of brain and central
nervous system functions.. 178

EEG studies are increasingly revealing 179

We are beginning to understand subcellular
electrochemical activity in the living brain
and nervous system 180

Brain-injured children are usually least impaired
in personality functioning 181

RNA seems to have much to do with our
remembering 182

Dyslexia generally reflects complex deficits in
the child 183

Prognosis may still be good 184

Abnormal function may rise out of chronic abnormal
process; function and process are a two-way high-
way 187

Chapter 12: SOME PHARMACOTHERAPY AIDS
ARE HERE NOW 189

We stand at a marvelous threshold 189

There are some dangers too 190

The right drugs bring improvement in emotional
stability 192

The neuropsychiatrist is often in the best position to
  direct the use of drugs with these children 195
Dilantin and Mesantoin 196
Librium 197
Equanil and Miltown 197
Meprospan 198
Benadryl 198
Benzedrine and Dexedrine 198
Atarax 199
Valium 199
Compazine 199
Stelazine 200
Mellaril 200
Tofranil 200
Suvren 201
Ritalin and newer drugs to come 202
Good teachers still are powerful influences 202
Chapter 13: PARENTS NEED WISE SUPPORT AND
  THERAPY TOO 203
Blaming does no one much good 203
Most mothers and fathers really want to learn 205
Textbook-lecture courses are no substitute for life
  experience 205
The residue of organicity can be discouraging 206
Some communities do not value good education 207
Too much advice, from too many quarters, can
  confuse and dishearten the best parents 208
There are delicate balances in a child's relationships
  with his parents 209
The teacher does not have to possess all the answers ... 210
The right honesty about a child can help 210
Good parent-teacher conferences are not difficult to
  manage 211
Children secretly know the truth about themselves;
  so do parents 212
Go slowly; be sincere; look out level 213

Talk about the child's good points; keep a large view... 214
Keep the doors wide open 215
Hold long range hope for every child 216
Chapter 14: EARLY RECOGNITION CAN AVERT
    SOME COMPLICATIONS 217
The right intervention, early enough to help most 217
The psychologist's task in a busy school 217
14-year-old's complicated life 218
Signals of cortical irritability 220
Signals of trouble in a child's WISC ratings 223
Glimpses of personality dynamics in test responses 223
Schools must step up to responsibilities 229
A more fortunate five-year-old who did have good
    help at the right times 230
The multidiscipline team at work effectively in
    the school 231
Chapter 15: INTIMATIONS OF IMPORTANT
    BREAKTHROUGHS JUST AHEAD 239
Our potentialities still are the most amazing
    phenomena in the universe 239
Hippocrates sensed this long ago 239
The intervening centuries have seen great strides . 240
Pierre Paul Broca's work 241
John Hughlings Jackson; Carl Wernicke; Ferrier 242
Pick, and Head; then Penfield 242
Sherrington's early discoveries.................................... 243
Cobb; Bertrand; Jasper 245
The brain's vast interarea networks............................. 246
Hyman L Lippman: difficult behavior and organicity... 247
Special education is taking on a new form 248
The brain has magnificent self-healing and self-
    recovery powers 249
Bright hope ahead for children, in all these advances ... 250
GLOSSARY OF SPECIAL TERMS 253

ILLUSTRATIONS

10 1/2-year-old girl, in grade 4: her drawing and
design 4
Two 11-year-olds: comparison of figure drawings ....6— 7
12-year-old, in grade 5, hyperactive: his reproduction
of designs 9
9-year-old, with probable organicity: his drawing of
a man 12
9-year-old girl, possible cerebral dysfunction: her draw-
ing of a man 15
8 1/2-year-old, in grade 3, quite jittery: his drawing of
a man 21
13-year-old, in grade 7, very nervous, speech difficulty:
drawing of man ....24— 25
10-year-old, in grade 3, severe reading trouble: draw-
ing of man 30
Two 12-year-olds: portions of their EEG tracings 44
11-year-old: his drawing of man, and best attempt to
copy design ....48— 49
Two 8-year-olds, one possibly schizophrenic: drawings
of man ....52— 53
10-year-old, with perceptual-motor damage: reproduc-
tion of design 64
11-year-old, in grade 5: handwriting and copying de-
signs ....68— 69
Some designs that may be used with children over 8 80
14-year-old boy, in junior high special class: repro-
duction of designs 81
Figure-background samples for use with children 82
10-year-old, in grade 4, with perceptual-motor trouble,
extensive school-learning difficulty: writing
samples .... 102—103
her object-assembly (WISC horse) attempt.................. 105

15-year-old, in grade 7, bright but with organic
    signs: his attempt to reproduce complex designs 108
15 1/2-year-old girl: reproduction of a man and a
    dog, and spelling attempts.....................................112—113
12-year-old who sustained severe head injury at 6:
    his attempt to write a paragraph about himself
    (compared with production of noninjured 12-
    year-old) 114
11-year-old, with subtle organicity: reproduction of
    designs from recall, by copying, and then by tracing... 117
12-year-old: example of typing that reflects perceptual-
    motor-expression trouble... 150
10-year-old: handwriting reflecting her subtle organ-
    icity 171
11-year-old, possible organicity: comparison of his
    reproduction of designs before medication, then
    with medication 193
Carol's EEG tracing, from left parietal cortex area 221
Her earlier, later drawings of herself ....224—226
Total scheme of the full school service team 237
Some divisions of the left hemisphere 244

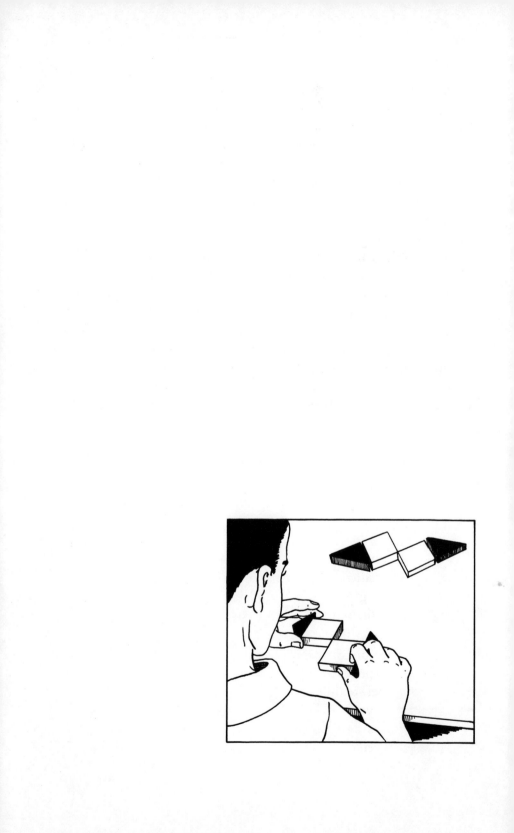

1

THESE ARE OUR
CHILDREN TOO . . .

One characteristic of boys and girls all around the world
stands out so plainly that it unites them into a single large
family: Children are adept at putting on bold fronts, even in
times of inner despair. Our children are experts at hiding secret discouragement, anxiety, and fear. The camouflage can be
almost perfect.

Every teacher and parent with much of a memory, plus an
alert eye and ear for the real lives of children, has caught
glimpses of children going all-out to make believe they never
feel hurt or afraid of anything.

Perhaps such efforts are marks, smudged by tears and
mixed with angry words at times, of the ultimate strength of
the human spirit. Perhaps such signs reflect a heritage of courage that can renew itself even after the darkest moments.

Whatever the meaning, our children often show a marvelous
kind of rugged resilience to the stresses of life. Otherwise many
youngsters would give up and quit trying long before the rest
of us had noticed the outer signals of discouragement.

For our children, like ourselves, have human limits of en-
durance. Chronic discouragement can turn the hardiest of us
from the high purposes and hopes we once held. You need not
have lived long before this fact of life is plain.

Jim could tell you. At 14, he has rediscovered it several
times. A few years ago, when he was just starting school, his
major problems centered around hyperactive behavior and the

perceptual-motor difficulties that frequently fill out this clinical picture. Now at 14, he has felt very discouraged about himself a long time.

His real name is not Jim, but it will do here. He represents a large population of boys and girls, as many as a quarter of the children in some communities, who have needed someone to speak up for them. These children are either failing outright, or are barely keeping ahead of failing.

If Jim could spell better, he could write his own book about such children. He certainly could add all the details out of his own experience. He is not a lazy boy who is satisfied to flounder through school. In the busy years I have worked as the psychologist in many schools, I have never seen a child who was happy about possible failure. Yet I have seen Jim warming the office bench a dozen times a week, with an odd kind of half-smile glued across his lips.

There he sat last Monday, trying to seem anything but discouraged, waiting for the vice-principal to open the door and invite him inside. Jim had arrived at math class—again without a book. "I don't know where it is," he insisted, "I haven't seen it in two weeks."

"What about the language arts book you told Miss Jenkins you can't find, Jim?"

"It's gone too."

I know Jim very well. He could honestly have added, "Suppose I did find the books, I still can't read them enough to manage the work. Everybody tells me I'm not dumb. Well, here I am in eighth grade, but fourth grade books are beyond me. The day brains were being passed out, I must have showed up with a bucket with a hole in the bottom to get my share . . . . No, I didn't say anything, I was just thinking to myself. . . but I sure feel discouraged . . . ."

By Thursday of practically any week, Jim has bluffed so much that even he is sick of it. "Why can't I drop out of school? That would make everybody happy. (Well, everybody except me, I guess. I don't often feel happy about me anymore. Every time I look around I can see how dumb I am. I'll be fifteen, but I won't be able to read well enough to get by fifth grade work. Mom and Dad have given up about me. Mom still nags me to do better in school so I will amount to something when I go to get a job, but she told my dad I was never very bright or I would have passed better in lower grades. If there was any place I could run away to, I'd do it now.")

In many ways Jim has been running away for a long time: by the lost books he never seems quite able to find; by arriving at classes just late enough to be sent to the front office for a note to readmit him; by thinking there would be no school today because it was raining so hard; by feeling too sick to go to math class, even though the school nurse and physician can find no symptoms that point to real physical trouble; by fooling around so much even in gym period and art that he is flunking these subjects too; and by a score of other ways, until this habit threatens to ruin his whole future.

Jim knows all this, although he has rarely admitted it openly to anyone else. He says he wants to do better and be more successful, but his best efforts to change seldom last beyond a week, then the old pattern is evident again. Most of his teachers secretly feel as hopelessly about the unhappy boy as he does about himself. Unless the right help comes soon, it will be too late to be of much benefit.

Early diagnosis, at least by third grade, would have been worth whatever effort it would have cost at the time. Thoughtful parents and school board members, as well as alert school people, know that good guidance and psychological services in elementary grades pay high dividends for the children in these grades.

Special Note:

Illustrations and case notes in this text are from the writer's files, over the last 15 years of clinical practice. Children's names have been changed, of course. Other details have been kept intact. Particularly in this Chapter, the illustrations take up full pages. The text continues following an illustration.

Some notes on a jittery youngster.* She was 10 1/2 then—in grade 4. This was the best drawing she could make of a man. The task took her nearly 10 minutes; she seemed to be putting all her ability into the drawing.

Her reading level was grade 3-0, with many reversals and misses. She had difficulty in finding the next line.

Her mother said the girl "was very nervous as a baby too. Used to kick hard in utero." The mother reported some spotting in early months of pregnancy.

The child stuttered severely at times. She was a very attractive girl, though quite easily upset even by mild excitement, and cried easily.

She had great difficulty in drawing a simple design from memory after short exposure. Here was her best achievement in reproducing one design:

86% actual size

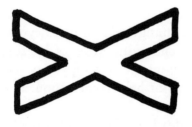

Her performance on the WISC reflected much better *verbal* than *performance* level. Her vocabulary score was slightly above average; comprehension a little higher. Digit span was very poor, especially in reverse order.

Her spelling was nearly average for her age. An older brother in grade 11, was getting along well there. "He was never nervous like this child," the mother said.

*This girl had been tentatively diagnosed as very neurotic, with marked learning disability. Her electroencephalogram was abnormal, showing diffuse dysrhythmia that reflected epilepsy. Before the careful neurological evaluation she had been labeled as a child who "needed to be made to behave better in school. . . ."

Here are some of the descriptive phrases every teacher (and parent) has heard that point to the children being considered in this book. The child in mind usually is a boy, but the list can include girls too.

——such a problem at times you hardly know how to cope with him
——seems above average in intelligence; maybe he lacks motivation
——has so much trouble in understanding what he has just read
——reads so poorly at times; often reverses words; even skips lines
——talks almost constantly at times without regard for others
——hardly seems to pay attention
——just does not follow directions
——so stubborn at times
——gets so upset and angry with the least provocation
——has great trouble in reading, not always comparable difficulty in arithmetic
——needs so much personal attention so much of the time
——seems to have a hearing problem, but not all the time
——can spell fairly well, yet seems unable to write words correctly
——participates so poorly in group activities
——needs such tight controls and limits to behave even moderately
——seems much more awkward and clumsy than other children the same age
——suddenly bucks all authority without apparent reason
——so easily distracted by the slightest thing

It is not difficult to realize why a youngster who shows even a half dozen such behavior characteristics can disrupt the usual classroom or household. Perfectly good teachers have said to me off the record, "Please take Jim out of my class, for awhile at least, until I can recover from the chronic sense of failure he has given me." Otherwise perfectly good mothers

5

Two 11-year-old girls were asked to draw a person. The first girl was just as nice a youngster as the second. Both were able to read at grade 5 level, but the first girl had great difficulty in recalling what she had just read.

This is how she drew "a man." She had a great deal of difficulty trying to reproduce a triangle from memory.

Her WISC responses showed wide scatter, from very poor on the Block-Designs to slightly above average on the Vocabulary subtest. Her medical history suggested possible oxygen shortage at birth, though this had not necessarily caused central nervous system trouble.

An older brother, 14, and two younger sisters, 7 and 9, were getting along fairly well in school. All were warmly valued and cared for in the family.

The second girl said she would rather draw a girl, and took 6 minutes to complete her sketch. She had no difficulty in reproducing geometric designs from memory . . . . On the WISC, her subtest scores were all close to average, with little spread.

Her mother said the child had never been a problem. The pregnancy and birth had been normal. The child's health history contained no notes of severe illness, high fever, or emotional upsets. She had had no extra art help, and she had never spent much time drawing.

From these drawings, which child would you expect might have more difficulty with school subjects?

have confessed to similar feelings. "I try so hard every day with that child, but it often seems hopeless. His father thinks we ought to be stricter with the boy, but that hasn't worked either. So I take more aspirin and muddle through my home-work-time each evening. There are days when I wonder what I ever did to cause this trouble. . . ."

The unhappy and discouraged children described in the following pages often include most of the failing group in a school. Sometimes they try so hard to do the work that you would wonder why they still are so unsuccessful. Many of the hyperactive and very sensitive youngsters I have seen wept when telling me how discouraged they felt about themselves. These same children would go by me in the hallways with cheery expressions on their faces. You might never guess their secret feelings if you just looked at them in a group.

Right here it must be said that many kinds of trouble can trip a child into unhappy behavior and unhappy reactions that may mask the deeper causes. One third-grader comes to my mind just now as a case in point. The teacher reported the child to be "so droopy and irritable just before lunch time that nobody wants her around at all." The rough home situation was first blamed, and then the difficulty of the late morning arithmetic class. The real culprit turned out to be hypoglyce-mia—low blood sugar. Adequate remedy of this deeper sys-temic problem soon brought a happier, less irritable young-ster.

Severe emotional stress can make children behave in ways that are hard to differentiate at times from a dozen kinds of *mental* conditions. Very upset and anxious children sometimes do so poorly in school that they may even seem quite retarded. Every teacher can remember trying to fathom such a young-ster. Emotions are powerful at times. They can be like the proverbial straw that broke the camel's back. Even by itself, heavy emotional stress can impair school progress. Added to deeper organic difficulties, emotional burdens can spell real trouble for any child.

8

This is how one hyperactive 12-year-old (with an IQ around 105) tried to reproduce simple designs from memory after 10-second exposures:

The Designs　　　　　　　　　　　How he reproduced them

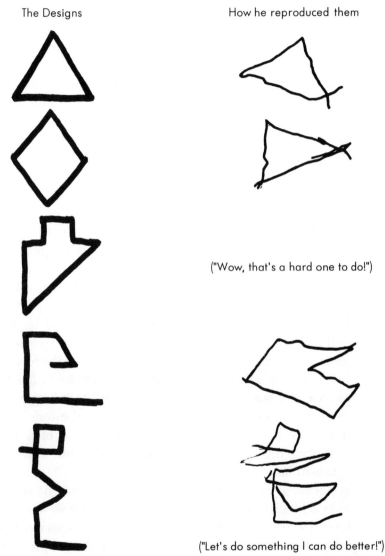

("Wow, that's a hard one to do!")

("Let's do something I can do better!")

85% actual size

This boy was in fifth grade, struggling to read at grade 2.5 level. Arithmetic was barely up to grade 3.0. Can you sense the kind of visual perception distortion he constantly faced?

Clinical experience in recent years with hyperactive children has been crystalizing out a broad composite syndrome of the characteristics of such youngsters. Commonly, such a child is apt to show many of these signs:

High distractibility — He may seem literally forced by some unusual sensitivity to respond to all sorts of extraneous stimuli, so he cannot give calm attention to the important matter at hand. A softly ticking clock in the room can so absorb his attention that what the teacher has just been saying may go completely unnoticed.

Marked motor disinhibition — Fingers just seem unable to resist exploring everything within reach. Feet wiggle and tap almost incessantly. A pencil or ruler swiftly becomes a drumstick on a desk top. Locker handles get rattled all down the line. Paper clips and rubber bands tempt irresistible experiments to zing special targets. Lips and tongue buzz and whistle and mimic.

Figure-background disturbances — The child may have real difficulty in perceiving the important parts of a picture apart from the rest of the page. When he is asked to notice the sailboat on a card viewed through a transparent plastic sheet covered with wave-like lines, he can hardly find the boat. When asked to copy the sailboat, he is apt to draw mostly the waves instead of the boat. A little speck on the card may capture his attention for several moments. A ticking clock or faint noises in the background may keep him from hearing what you are trying to tell him, even when he wants to hear you.

High tendency toward perseveration — He may have considerable difficulty in shifting from one situation to another. This characteristic may be evident when he has been working several minutes to copy a relatively simple design in colored blocks. When these children are able to get the design just right, they sometimes keep going in *more* trials! They seem unable to recognize when their work is right.

Marked distortion of visual perception — These children often have trouble in reproducing simple designs from memory after short exposures. Some may hardly be able to copy the designs directly. The basic difficulty in such a youngster is not in his eyes but in the cortical (and perhaps subcortical) area of his brain that must *translate* the electrical impulses arriving from the retinae into what we call vision. His eyes perform well enough, but the visual cortex may sum up the impulses into very distorted percepts. Such a problem certainly can make reading and writing terrifically difficult for any child.

Marked distortion of other perceptual facets — Tactile and auditory distortions may also be present (though not always as clearly apparent) in these children. Recent studies have been revealing disturbances of taste and smell in addition to visual-auditory-motor-tactile difficulties in many hyperactive boys and girls.

Marked distortion of self-image — Sometimes this is reflected by the child when he is asked to draw the best picture he can make of a person. Many of the drawings such youngsters have made reflect severe distortions of the human figure, with arms and legs all extending out of a head. Children with marked distortions in body-image are apt to find great difficulty in learning to read. Extensive research is supporting this fact.

Marked confusion of laterality — Before a child can begin to draw well and learn to read well, he needs to mature to where he can easily distinguish between his left side and his right, and can control the two sides of his body separately. Without good laterality development, he may not develop good directionality and good kinesthetic awareness, or correct space perception. All these are very important basic abilities necessary for learning to read well.

Emotional disturbances — It is not hard to imagine why a child who lives in tight contact with daily frustration about all sorts of perceptual and motor trouble sometimes gets very upset, especially in school situations where accuracy of per-

11

A 9-year-old fourth-grader drew this figure of a man for me.

He was an attractive looking boy, usually pleasant and cooperative, trying hard to "be good in school." He was barely able to manage grade 1.5 reading; arithmetic about grade 2.5 level. His rating on the revised Stanford-Binet was IQ 80.

He often seemed very jittery and nervous in the afternoons and just couldn't sit still. "Into so many difficulties every week," the teacher had noted. "He's so hard to calm down, yet he is not a slow child intellectually. He is far brighter than the tests have shown. . . ."

Two electroencephalograms a month apart helped to clarify some of the possibilities beneath the boy's jitteriness. The EEG report from the hospital pointed to probable organicity: Basic frequency very poorly defined, about 7 per second. Fast waves at times, perhaps of muscle origin. For a few minutes no paroxysmal activity in the record, but occasional 5 per second waves were noted in areas of frontal bilateral leads. Hyperventilation greatly increased slow waves in occipital areas.

Impression of the physician-electroencephalographer: Considerable generalized abnormal cerebral activity. Cortex probably somewhat "stormy" and irritable much of the time.

Clinical psychologist's impression of the lad: Somewhat above average in potential. Should do best in good special class for children with perceptual-motor difficulties.

By 14, this boy had learned to read at grade 4 level. His WISC intelligence rating at that time was 122.

ceiving and responding are so important to success. Emotional difficulties are so commonplace in these children that these upsets and blocks have sometimes been thought to be causal. Certainly they can add to whatever deeper dysfunction has existed, to complicate diagnosis of the child's situation.

Keeping in mind at least the possibility of organicity in children with somewhat chronic behavior problems can guard us from tumbling for easy-do panaceas that flash across the educational horizons at times as sure cures for learning troubles. Careful studies have been revealing that there are no simple remedies for severe school disabilities, especially when the trouble may be rising out of organic dysfunctions or defects. Experienced teachers know that guarded hopefulness, undergirding a warm experimental attitude toward children's learning difficulties, is much better than accepting one remedial technique as a panacea for every youngster in every class situation.

Parents often need the same wise guarding, particularly in these days when articles and ads in popular magazines are promoting dozens of *new* methods to teach children to read better, manage schoolwork better, and behave better in general. Most parents I have had an opportunity to try to help with complex problems about their children genuinely wanted to do whatever was best in the case. The most difficult question to fathom was: Just what *is* best?

2

SOME DIFFERENTIALS ABOUT THESE CHILDREN . . .

There have always been children who seem unable to learn very well, even with special help. These children used to be cataloged simply as slow and then forgotten. But thanks to happier concepts and better methods, this picture is swiftly changing. It is heartening to find old superstitions about such children losing the power they once held over teachers and parents. If you make a statement such as these about a child now, somebody is likely to draw you up short and question your knowledge:

"Fred simply doesn't *want* to learn."

"Sharon doesn't even try to behave better."

"Tom's mother is the whole trouble."

"Kids who can't do the work just ought to flunk out of school."

"School is easy enough now that any boy or girl could get by with a little steady effort."

"Teachers pamper them too much."

Clearer insight is setting us free to see all boys and girls (and parents) in a warmer, more hopeful light. And this change is having wonderful effects on many schools in many places. Good teachers now are alert to subtle signals of perceptual-motor difficulties in children's drawings, for example, so that these youngsters are seen in a brighter light.

Drawing of a man, by a hyperactive 9-year-old, in grade 3.

Rated on the new Goodenough-Harris scale, the drawing would place this girl far below normal intelligence.

Yet on the WISC this child rated considerably above average on the full scale (IQ 110). On the verbal subtests, her rating was 116, and 92 on the performance subtests.

The child had been "extremely nervous" until she was five, the mother reported. "A feeding problem too! We hope to find a tutor who can help her begin to read better."

The teacher had noted: "Very jittery at times. Hard to get her to settle down to work. Often irritable. Negative too. Not like others in her group. Yet she is a pretty child; hard to dislike very long."

This child showed many subclinical signs of possible cerebral injury or dysfunction. Her deep tendon reflexes were increased and unequal. General motility was slightly awkward for a child her age and size. When she was

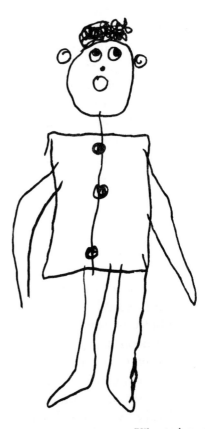

78% actual size

asked to close her eyes and hold her arms outstretched, her arms quickly spread and lowered considerably. The little fingers were spread wide from the rest of the hands; Paul Schilder regarded this as a sign reflecting possible cerebellar damage.

This little girl presented a real puzzle to the school. The breakthrough came when the teacher called in the psychologist and together they tackled the task of diagnosing the real trouble. The next three years in an excellent class for children with perceptual difficulties found great improvement in this youngster.

There are many possible causes of brain dysfunction. The life stage at which the injury occurs in a child's development can be an important factor in how the injury will affect his school career. The earlier an injury happens and thus impedes normal development of that area of the cortex, the greater may be the results in lowered learning abilities in the child.

The same cortical injury in different children may not bring the same degree of learning deficits or behavior difficulties, although the effects will often be quite similar. Just as some children can withstand worse bruises than other youngsters, and survive worse infections with less damage than other children, so may one child come through a cerebral trauma and recover much better than another child. Many parts of the brain, like many other parts of the human organism, are remarkably self-restoring and self-reestablishing.* We can well consider ourselves blessed by such inborn powers, for none of us otherwise would come to adult years with much intelligence or ability of any kind!

Encouraging evidence has been coming to light recently to indicate that the central nervous system, including the brain, can gradually *re-wire* and *re-circuit* itself to circumvent past injuries and damage that were not too severe or too extensive. Truly, we have been wonderfully created. Even the slowest learner in town is still a marvelously complex and capable person, rightfully deserving warmest respect and consideration from all of us. The least able child still is priceless.

Oxygen deprivation that persists longer than a few minutes can severely damage important cortical areas. Such a shortage of oxygen during birth has injured some children. Multiple births sometimes involve this hazard, though not as much for the infant who is born first. Breach presentation sometimes involves anoxia in the baby. A cord wrapped around a little neck can be hazardous to life. Some researchers now believe

---

*One purpose of this book is to point out such capacity to recover, even while keeping in mind the inherent vicissitudes and dangers children face in growing to maturity. *(Note: The brain is part of the central nervous system.)*

that intracranial hemorrhage at birth hurts more children than once thought by many obstetricians. In the widespread effort to relieve mothers of pain at labor, some children have been endangered by anesthesia for the mother. Some excellent pain reducers for the mother at labor can cross over the placenta in sufficient concentration to be hazardous to the baby.

Childhood diseases that once were thought to be quite harmless are now being suspected of causing minimal neurological injuries that sometimes have aftereffects in mild behavior and learning trouble. Many toxins—both endogenous and exogenous—that were somewhat suspect before as causes of trouble are now known to be very dangerous to the brain and central nervous system.

Some toxins are much more dangerous to nervous tissue than others. The ingestion of minute quantities of lead, for example, have been known to bring severe, extensive central nervous system damage in some children before the deadly agent could be counteracted. There may be many commonly employed chemicals that are potentially much more dangerous than once guessed.

Biological scientists are now quite aware that virus infections can trigger subtle but still lethal changes in the body's organ systems long after the primary invasions themselves have vanished.

The body is marvelously comprised of many intricate organ systems that have scores of complex interorgan managing and sustaining functions. Some of these multi-biochemical functions are just beginning to be understood for what they really are and do for us, in rebuilding tissues, releasing energy fuels, and oxidizing and reconstituting the myriad chemical substances we need to live. Slight dysfunction of any organ system can result in widespread trouble. Remember that gallbladder upset, or that appendix reaction?

Physicians can now recognize the signs of deadly phenylketonuria—PKU, in medical parlance—in time to rectify this dysfunction in the newborn child. PKU used to leave its innocent little victims hopelessly damaged intellectually before parents suspected something must be wrong. Now a relatively simple test administered shortly after birth promptly reveals PKU and makes effective treatment an easy matter, so that the baby is swiftly lifted out of the old danger.

Medical science is making remarkable strides in new knowledge and skills to rectify other dangerous dysfunctions and imbalances, before irreversible nervous system injury has happened. We still face many great problems on these scientific frontiers, but we have come a long way in the last twenty-five years.

The day may be not far ahead when scientist-researchers in biology and neurology will be able to give physicians and surgeons new chemicals and new techniques to remedy and even prevent most of the neurological damage and dysfunction now suspected to be at the base of some behavior and learning difficulties in many children.

How can teachers (and parents) discern children who feel very jittery much of the time and may be headed for failure in our present classrooms? What are the early signs in such boys and girls that we can note soon enough to get the help that may be needed in these cases?

First of all, we need to keep clearly in mind the wide range of characteristics often exhibited by children who seem quite hyperactive, whether these children can be clearly shown to demonstrate central nervous system impairment or not. Some hyperactive children show many signs of psychopathology in very marked degrees. These girls and boys usually are easy to spot.

There are other children with known central nervous system impairment or injury who do not show many of the expected signs. Discerning the mildly hyperactive child who may be reacting to minimal central nervous system disturbance or injury requires careful procedure. The next few years will undoubtedly bring better clinical techniques to aid in spotting

18

such children earlier and more reliably than now possible. Professional journals, particularly in neurology and clinical psychology, are reporting new techniques and instruments all the time. This certainly is a hopeful sign that we are gaining headway on one of the major problems—accurate, early recognition.

Discovering some of the *signs* of hyperactivity in a child should not make the teacher or parent feel certain of this possibility without the clinical confirmation of the psychologist. This precaution is needed to avoid using the hyperactive classification as a catchall for every child who may occasionally exhibit some jittery signs or behavior. I have known many good teachers, however, who could draw upon their teaching experience over several years—plus alert study in special workshop sessions on children with possible brain injuries—who could spot hyperactive youngsters very well. The *hit scores* of these teachers often were above the 80% level. Within the range of reasonable cautions, thoughtful, experienced teachers can discern major signs of the jittery child who should be referred for further examination and evaluation.

In some classroom groups of children that I can remember, there were as many as one child in five or six who seemed hyperactive enough for this basic difficulty to account for much of the youngster's poor school showing. This ratio—sometimes as high as one child in five—should not surprise any administrator or teacher in whose school one-fourth of the seventh- and eighth-graders must struggle hard to avoid outright failure.

In those same classrooms few children seemed genuinely disturbed enough emotionally to account in large measure for their impending failure. There were children who needed adequate professional help to surmount emotional handicaps, and some of these children were not up to par academically. A higher proportion of referrals seemed hyperactive, with or without demonstration of brain injury, and with or without emotional overlay.

19

Children who are hyperactive are apt to feel somewhat upset emotionally at times. This is understandable enough. If the keys on the organ you were playing suddenly changed their connections to the pipes right while you were trying to play the concerto you thought you had mastered, you might feel upset emotionally too. Some hyperactive children experience comparable troubles all day long. Little wonder these boys and girls seem irritable at times. If you found nearly constant difficulty in keeping the incoming signals from your eyes, ears, fingers, and a million other nerves in clear order in your jittery brain, you might feel discouraged and disinterested too. Thinking about this a moment brings us closer to understanding jittery children.

Injury even to a minute part of the brain can affect many functions we commonly consider as *centering* mainly in other areas. One child whose brain may have been slightly injured— or may never have developed proper cellular functions and neural interconnections—may display a surprisingly wide array of behaviorial peculiarities.

Another child with an apparently comparable injury or defect might show far less difficulty. These differences are beginning to be understood in the light of new explorations of the brain and central nervous system.

Here are some of the signs that are helpful in discerning the jittery or hyperactive children at home or in school.

The parent may describe the child in such sentences as these:

——He is so different from my other children at times.

——I love him as much as the others, but he is harder to manage.

——He wanted to go to school, but he has been a problem there.

——He lacks confidence in himself much of the time.

——Yes, he's often very touchy and jittery.

——When he gets sick, he's apt to be terribly sick.

—— So many little things seem to upset him so much.

——We surely need help with him, there are days when I'm

Drawing of a man, by a handsome boy 8 1/2, in third grade at the time. His drawing scored slightly below average on the Goodenough-Harris scale. Notice particularly the distortions and omissions. The drawing was better in some ways than this sensitive but jittery child might have been expected to do. The figure reflects many of the signals seen in the drawings of children with mild to severe degrees of cerebral difficulty.

On the WISC, this boy showed above-average intellectual potential hindered by perceptual-motor difficulties. On the *verbal* subtests he rated 121 IQ; on the *performance* section he rated 89.*

His reading was very poor, and the teacher noted *thought process* trouble.

He had been delivered by caesarean section, with no complications except that the cord had been around the neck in utero. How much this may have affected the brain's development was impossible to answer.

When this boy was seen by the psychologist at 8 1/2, the general behavior picture was that of a very excitable lad who was rarely angry

76% actual size

but usually quite jittery. His mother said the boy was much better than he used to be. Teachers had reported: "Seldom quiet," "Not a naughty child, but what a chore to manage," "Gets into everything. . . ."

*This high a verbal-performance differential is not seen in every child who may have sustained cerebral injury.

ready to give up . . . . I used to think it was just my
fault. . . .

Teachers' comments may reflect the child's picture too:

——He is a bright enough child for our school, but he has not
been able to settle down enough to learn very well.

——She is a happy enough child, but so inattentive at times.

——He shouldn't be passed, perhaps, but retaining him might
not help much; after all, his IQ of 104 ought to mean he
can learn.

——Sometimes he won't even try; other times he can do fairly
well. Why does he vary so much?

——This child has baffled me by his reading trouble, yet he
can do arithmetic better.

——The slightest things distract him completely at times.

——He seems almost unable to change whatever he is doing.

——The class gets so angry at him, I feel sorry for him.

——Somehow I know he could do better, but tests just wreck
him.

——At times I feel he hardly hears, but this varies . . . .

Thoughtful neighbors often see this child in a similar light:

——He is so noisy . . . and so active . . . he's seldom still.

——He likes to go to the store for me, but I never am sure he
will bring back what I told him I needed.

——I don't think I'd know what to do with him if he were
mine.

——I tried to help him read, but my methods seemed fruitless.

——He helped us paint the new fence last year, but he had as
much paint on himself. . . .

The gym teacher may see some important aspects:

——He is never quite sure what hand or foot is left or right.

——She is much clumsier than other youngsters this age.

——He becomes confused in a fast game.

——He seems a little immature in physical structure.

Test performances may reflect the same deeper troubles:

——She often rates better on *verbal* than on *performance* tests.

—— Complicated directions often tangle him up very much.
—— Sometimes he comes out worse on group tests.
—— He rates better on a *picture* type vocabulary test.
—— He seems to know the answers but can't find the right words.
—— She is unable to repeat several digits in reversed order; can't seem to remember what digits were given.
—— He does better on a test given to him alone in a quiet room.

The art teacher's comments may reveal a similar picture:
—— His space perception is very inadequate; his form perception is just as poor.
—— He seems unable to break a pattern he has used a little while.
—— Vivid colors sometimes seem to disturb him quite a bit.
—— His drawings often reflect rigidity. Some of them seem quite bizarre, with many signs of anxiety and frustration.
—— Last week, he just quit in the middle of the art lesson. When I asked what the trouble might be, he looked discouraged as he answered, "Nothing I draw is right, so I quit."

Most brain-injured children are quite impulsive and are apt to act hastily just on the spur of the moment, with little thought or planning. Perhaps they are so impulsive because they have poor inner controls. Yet, every impulsive youngster is not necessarily brain-injured. Impulsiveness is evident in some children who simply have developed neurotic behavior and are upset. Careful diagnosis is a must in all these cases.

Compulsiveness is one of the best defenses children sometimes devise to manage deeper impulsivity. Compulsiveness can be part of the neurotic behavior picture too, even in jittery children who use this method to manage excessive hyperactive tendencies. One of the signals of this duality of impulsivity-compulsivity in many children is the high drive to make practically every task rigidly routine and tackle each job with draggy deliberation. The youngster who has to spend an ex-

Drawing of a man, by a 13-year-old boy, in grade 7.

The teacher said he was "very nervous, highstrung, and hard to get down to the job." His mother said the boy was "a rough behavior problem much of the evenings at home. When he's tired, he gets terribly nervous and fights the other children over every little thing."

He was reading at grade 6.0 level, but with many reversals and halts. About average in arithmetic; WISC IQ—full scale—114, verbal subtests—130, performance subtests—90.

His responses were very poor on the Goldstein-Scheerer block-design series, reflecting perceptual difficulties.

His health history noted a severe pneumonia at age 3.6, that left the child prostrated. He remained apathetic for a long time afterward. "He seems so different, not at all like our boy," the mother had said.

His speech was lisping, slurring, and dysrhythmic. It sounded slovenly but actually took the child's very best efforts. There was some shaking of his outstretched hands.

His drawing of a man reflected a self-image level below his WISC performance IQ, and certainly much below his verbal test level on the WISC. Some signs of personality disturbance were present.

Gross difficulty in drawing a man (especially when the drawing is much below the child's mental age level) often reflects body-image imperception that has cerebral localization. Some researchers have felt the discrepancy reflects possible damage or dysfunction of the angular gyrus. Paul Schilder, in his classical studies of such children at Bellevue Hospital a few years ago, strongly felt this was so.

cessive amount of time and energy on relatively simple projects or assignments probably is struggling hard against underlying impulsivity.

Children with such behavior characteristics often are widely misjudged at the moment. The task of teaching a class with even a few jittery children in it day by day can be exasperating to the wisest teacher. When such a boy or girl seems to be above average in some ways intellectually—and many of them do—this fact understandably complicates the picture to confuse the best parent (or teacher).

These jittery youngsters sometimes behave quite neurotically, showing many of the clinical signs of moody discouragement, anxiety, gloomy fantasies, shame, and guilt, along with a peculiar *need* to feel punished or downgraded. These signals may not always be clearly visible, unless the child is suffering severely.

Such a child should not surprise us when he seems at first to distrust almost everyone who tries to help him.

The following Table may be helpful in understanding some of the differentials between *children who are quite jittery (hyperactive) and have perceptual-motor difficulties that interfere with school progress, and other children who have just developed slowly and thus find school difficult.*

Children in either of these groups need not show all the signals noted in the Table. Neither are the differentials always clearly defined in a particular child. The purpose of the Table is simply to encourage thoughtful teachers to perceive some of the *troubles* that many boys and girls face.

Note that the term *slower developers* is used, rather than retarded children or mentally deficient children.

DIFFERENTIALS	SOME HYPERACTIVE CHILDREN	SOME SLOWER DEVELOPERS
Broad impression such a child often gives	Often very restless, touchy, tense. Poor school marks out of line with apparent intelligence. A likeable youngster in many ways. "Challenging, but hard to manage in a busy classroom." "So easily upset at times." "Can't seem to remember what he learned a few days ago."	Usually fairly calm, easygoing. Not hard to teach, though somewhat slow. Usually retains what he does learn, just catches on at a slower pace. Inclined to roll with the ship.
General emotional stability	Impulsive; perhaps even "flighty" at times. Hard to guess what is bugging him at times. May not be able to tell you, himself. Hard to settle down sometimes.	Few emotional problems, if any. Easy to get settled down to steady work in the classroom.
Feelings of security about himself	Often seems anxious, afraid, insecure—just as often without apparent reason.	Generally seems to feel quite secure; not easily frightened. Recovers from fear swiftly enough.
Sense of personal value	So often rates himself poorly, even in light of better facts. "How can I be bright when I am so stupid in everything?"	This child is apt to rate himself well, though he usually is aware of his slower capacities in some subject areas.
Ability to disregard the actual classroom distractions	Sometimes very easily distracted by slightest sounds, light flickers, activities in the room— even his own thoughts. "How can anybody work in a place like this? I give up!"	Not bothered much. May even work harder because the group around him is busy too. "I like it this way, then I do better."
Sensitivity to correction or criticism	Readily dumped into moody feelings of discouragment and fear (though he may seldom be able to admit this). These feelings may be hard for him to clear.	Apt to show some resentment to needless criticism that he does not understand. Yet he can feel warmly valued anyway. Can usually clear resentful feelings with a little help.
Reaction to possibilities of failure	May secretly fret about such things, even after good counseling and warm encouragement.	This child can often take such troubles into stride surprisingly well. He is not apt to fret very long about things he knows he can't do much to change.
Effect of pressure to "do better"	Reaction sometimes far out of line with the actual pressure. "I am so jittery now I can't do anything at all . . . ."	"Well, I just do the best I can, that's all anybody can expect me to do . . . ."

DIFFERENTIALS	SOME HYPERACTIVE CHILDREN	SOME SLOWER DEVELOPERS
Unusual periods of tension, fussiness	Often come "out of clear skies," with little apparent cause in the environment. "I just feel nervous and touchy; go 'way and let me alone."	May have such periods but they are short in duration and infrequent. Can tell you why he was upset or touchy.
Apparent tendency to worry	Rather high. Often is a severe worrier. "I get mad at myself for worrying like I do, but the habit gets me down anyway."	Slight, if any. "Why should I worry, what good would it do me?"
General motor coordination	Sometimes very poor, though this is not always the case. May vary from day to day. This child usually is very much aware of his awkwardness and poor muscular skills. Often far below where his *general intelligence level* would indicate as likely.	Usually quite in line with his physical development. May do quite well in some shop projects that interest him.
Ability to discriminate left from right	This child often is very unsure. "Tell me slower so I don't get so mixed up when I try to do it."	In line with general mental development level.
Vocabulary and comprehension level	These may reflect his best potentials. "I can tell you better than I can write it down for you."	In line with general mental development level. (This youngster may not be much interested in words and composition anyway.)
Reading ability level	This boy or girl sometimes finds great difficulty in learning to read well, no matter what method is employed to help. Surprisingly enough, the child may be able to manage longer words than shorter ones, at times.	Difficulty usually quite in line with real mental level and social interests.
Arithmetic ability level	Trouble here may range from slight to great.	Math often is his poorest school mark.
Ability to reproduce simple designs from memory	Often markedly poor, yet not really bizarre. His drawings may rate far below his vocabulary and comprehension level. (His own awareness of this disparity sometimes adds emotional problems.)	Whatever difficulty he shows is likely to be in line with his general ability level. (This child may be able to draw much better than he can read.)

DIFFERENTIALS	SOME HYPERACTIVE CHILDREN	SOME SLOWER DEVELOPERS
Ability to distinguish figure from ground, in visual, auditory, and tactual patterns	This child frequently finds great difficulty here. He may not be sure even when his responses are quite correct.	In line with general mental development level and interest at the moment.
Ability to understand and work with simple devices, machines	Sometimes very poor. This may discourage him too. "Can't I do anything right?"	The shop teacher may say, "Just give him time, he can do many jobs very well . . . ."
Involvement with bizarre or peculiar behavior	Often worse when he feels upset or discouraged. "Yet I know he is not psychotic," his teachers will tell you.	This child's responses are more in line with those of younger boys and girls.

Careful study of the Table on the previous pages, especially with several real children in mind for comparisons, will help to bring the broad clinical differentials outlined in the two columns into sharper focus.

In my own clinical experience, I can remember only a few children who seemed to be simple cases of familial deficit or markedly slow development. Many children who were referred for help because someone felt they were *very retarded* turned out to be more like the child who drew the picture of a man reproduced on the next page. His responses to a children's adaptation of the Bender Visual-Motor Gestalt Test had alerted the physician to the possibility of cerebral injury. The boy had been seen several months earlier at a child guidance center; strong suggestions had been given to his mother that she was largely at fault for his extremely jittery behavior. She was told, "Love him more, scold him less, be more accepting, then he will begin to feel like a better child . . . ." The neurologist who examined the boy said the largest part of the problem stemmed from brain dysfunction, although the youngster's drawings also sometimes showed emotional problems threading through the clinical picture, complicating the picture even more.

The clinical problem of anxiety contaminating a child's test

Drawing of a man, by an attractive but jumpy boy nearly 10, in grade 3.

He had severe reading trouble; this gradually alleviated, perhaps because the child was put on special medication by the family physician.

A year before, the mother said, "He can burn up all the energy he has and still keep going. No matter how weary he seems, he still rushes around."

Child rated above average on the WISC *verbal* subtests, but poorer on *performance* subtests.

On the Taylor-Dobson test (reproduction of designs) he showed subtle signs of left hemisphere dysfunction. This was much better than he used to do on this test before medication helped him feel less jittery.

His responses on the Bender Visual-Motor Gestalt test reflected similar signs.

Marked improvement in schoolwork came with new teacher's warmer insight and control, including methods to reduce extraneous stimulation.

This boy is in tenth grade now, in a special program for such boys and girls. He has gained real confidence and courage about himself.

When he drew the man's head, he stopped a moment to say, "There's not much of a brain in his head—I'm the same way sometimes."

82% actual size

30

responses has not been an easy one to untangle, but carefully controlled studies have been throwing brighter light on the matter. Children with suspected brain dysfunction still deserve warm care and insight on the part of the clinician, in order to minimize the effect of anxious feelings regarding test performance. A good teacher knows how to establish the rapport which will enable a child to do his best.

Slight anxiety has been shown to have very little effect on a child's test performance. Mild anxiety in children who are not brain-injured makes little or no difference on their test performances. Brain-injured youngsters often feel somewhat anxious and sometimes agitated, but these factors disrupt test performance only in severe cases or when rapport is very poor.

Many children who are very poor readers exhibit a broad spectrum of imperception: visual, auditory, tactile, even sometimes taste and smell distortions. This gives some hint of the deeper problems that are involved, particularly in reading and arithmetic, that are highly symbolic. Remedial techniques that work well with one child may not be as helpful with another.

Because eye imperfections can impair a child's reading ability, such possibilities should always be kept in mind in any case. Much reading disability, however, in a child with only slight visual problems, should be viewed as one more signal of possible subtle brain dysfunctions. Intensive research for effective ways to help such children is greatly needed.

Within the last fifteen years, more and more studies have been revealing the marvelous *division of labor* in the human brain. For a long time we have known that the whole brain and central nervous system function as an integrated team to manage all the complicated aspects that we commonly call *the mind* and *the personality*. Now we know that slight injury to any part of the brain can have diffuse effects on functions that may not be dominantly centered in the injured area.

Each hemisphere seems to have its own work to do. The nondominant hemisphere (right hemisphere, in right-sided children) contains the *tonality* area so necessary in singing and in sonorous speech. Many researchers now feel that there is clear evidence of *interhemisphere confusion* in many cases of children with severe reading trouble, rather than strong left hemisphere *dominance* as in children who are learning to read fairly well.

These new concepts of brain-area functions are quite in line with such extensive research on dominant hemisphere localization carried out so dramatically at the Montreal Neurological Institute a few years ago by Dr. Wilder Penfield and Dr. Lamar Roberts. Their book, *Speech and Brain Mechanisms* is well worth careful study, particularly Chapter 9 on the evidence from cortical excision. The illustrations in the book paralleling detailed discussions of specific cortical areas that have to do with speech (and thinking) will be exciting to read for alert teachers who have a scientific flair.

We are entering a new era of knowledge about ourselves that will make us see even more clearly *how wonderfully we are made.* Threadbare phrases, such as how slow-learning a girl or boy seemed to be, are being replaced—at least among people who are keeping abreast of neurological research frontiers —by better insight and understanding that says how marvelously well the child does, in light of the deeper problems he may be facing.

Important advances are being made in clearer knowledge of the intricate structure and function of the human central nervous system and all its supporting organ systems. For example, recent psychological studies are corroborating earlier hypotheses that children who sustained left hemisphere injuries tend to show different intellectual difficulties than children with right hemisphere injuries. These studies have been no small breakthrough. True, the differences discovered are not dramatically great in all instances, but they have been demonstrated in other careful studies, including those reported by Ralph Rietan and his fellow researchers at Indiana University Medical Center.

Impairment of *verbal* abilities in a child are associated primarily with lesions of the *left* hemisphere (usually in Broca's area or Wernicke's area: refer to page 244). Abilities that require *comprehension of spatial and temporal relationships* are impaired primarily by lesions of the *right* hemisphere (generally in parieto-occipital regions). Localized injury of the frontal lobes does not appear to impair perceptual-motor capacities very much.

Children with marked difficulty in copying designs or assembling simple objects, for example, but who have less trouble with vocabulary and comprehension tests, might have sustained some injury to the right side of the brain that did not impair the left hemisphere. Thus, two children—one with left hemisphere injury and the other with right hemisphere injury— might earn the same full-scale IQ rating on such a test as the WISC, yet show quite different subtest profiles, with widely different meanings.*

The new era now opening in biochemistry will swiftly expand the frontiers of our knowledge of the human brain and nervous system. An important part of this new knowledge will surely encompass the application of surgical techniques and drugs not yet discovered. Radically new ways will be discovered, I believe, not only to alleviate but even to prevent many of the brain injuries now considered as the *normal risks* in getting born and growing up.

Every teacher has a vital part in this era of new hope for such children, by warmly exemplifying the paramount concept that all children have special value and deserve special care and help in coming to fullest stature in life.

Elementary teachers are in a particularly good position to discern the signs of the jittery child early enough to do the most to help him *before* he has added emotional problems to the primary ones. The earlier the referral, the better.

Reading disability has long been the Achilles' heel for many boys and girls in school. There are good reasons to believe that part of this school trouble so prevalent in many school

*See Carol's case, page 222.

systems in America has been related to the wide acceptance of *sight* methods instead of *phonetic* methods. The lower frequency of reading disability in schools in Germany, for example, may be related to more common use of phonetic teaching methods, plus more rational phonetic spelling of the language.

Reading disability may be a specific difficulty in a child. This should be suspected particularly in cases where children seem to have difficulty mostly in reading and spelling, with little or no trouble in arithmetic and number comprehension. Wider developmental difficulties may involve more of the child's school abilities in the picture.

Diagnostic possibilities such as general retardation, ocular and visual defects and dysfunctions, and emotional blocking must always be checked carefully, in any case, to avoid misjudging and misunderstanding the child. This point cannot be emphasized here too strongly. (In my own experience as the psychologist in schools with thousands of children, I cannot recall many youngsters who were just slow mentally, with no other organic or emotional difficulty, who did not learn to read somewhat in line with the mental-age level. Children rating much below IQ 80 on carefully administered intelligence tests such as the Stanford-Binet or the WISC have always seemed to me to reflect deeper difficulties, perhaps emotional or organic, even when the trouble was not clearly apparent to me.)

The beginning of the century was seeing scientific interest in reasons why some children have so much difficulty in learning to read. The British Medical Journal, in 1896, carried W. P. Morgan's insightful article on a case of what then was thought to be congenital word-blindness. A year earlier, Hinselwood in England had reported on his survey of acquired word-blindness in adults. One famous sufferer was John Hunter who was seventeen before he was able to read. Diagnosis in these early cases was greatly handicapped by lack of accurate neurological insight and knowledge. The present decade is witnessing the swiftest spurt in this field.

34

Careful studies in recent years reveal nearly a quarter of the children in many communities are not able to read at their proper school-grade level, yet they can manage better in other subjects that do not depend much on reading. Of course these boys and girls (most of them are boys) are likely to make poor showings on any *intelligence tests* demanding ability to read. Less thoughtful people used to feel that reading difficulty was simply an indication of lower mental ability. Fortunately this attitude is diminishing in most places, along with the idea that children who are failing in school "probably are not intelligent enough."

It is not surprising to experienced teachers that many children who have reading difficulty were considered to be bright until they entered school. In fact, the findings from several studies have intimated that very bright children need special teaching methods to help them *slow down* and learn to scan the printed page as must be done—line by line—to be able to read what is there. This situation probably does not annoy children having an IQ below 140, however. In the usual cases of reading trouble, other causes are more likely.

The typical clinical picture presented by poor readers sometimes begins without much evidence of the extent of the deeper causes in the child. He just seems slower in starting to read than some children. This may be the only notation on his records in some progressive schools until perhaps third grade. The real disability remains quite unrecognized in many children until complicating behavior problems appear and force sharper clinical attention.

Abnormalities in lateral dominance are commonplace in these children. Ambidexterity and mixed dominance—as right-handedness and left-eyedness—are frequently found in studying these boys and girls. R. S. Eustis found a very high percentage of left-eyedness, amphiocularity (sighting with either eye), and crossed laterality in the same group of poor readers. Half of these children had speech disturbances also. Late onset of talking is often found in the histories of children who have great difficulty in learning to read.

A high proportion of these children seem abnormally clumsy and poor in motor-coordination. Their movements are often jerky and unsmooth, as though the growing body were too far ahead of the nervous system in development. Printing and writing may be very poor. The child may be unable to participate in some games that require accuracy and speed of muscle response. No wonder so many of these children seem anxious and unhappy in school. What else could really be expected?

Many researchers along the line, including A. A. Silver in 1951, have pointed out how closely the clinical picture of very poor readers matches that of children who sustained cerebral injury. Many of the signs noticed in one group are found in the other: Immaturity of muscle responses, confused dominance and poor right-left discrimination, impairment of body-image and finger schema, general perceptual distortion or impairment, and marked difficulty in figure-ground separation.

Many of these neurological difficulties and imperfections can be remedied if noticed early enough in the child. There are solid findings in hundreds of studies that clearly indicate this hopeful goal to be even more attainable with younger children. Every teacher should be alert—particularly with children in primary grades—for any signals of perceptual-motor trouble. Prompt referral of these children for expert diagnosis and help can circumvent years of discouragement and failure. Many schools have been busy proving this with their own children.

Every community has its share of children with sufficient perceptual-motor involvement to hamper school progress to some degree. The recognized incidence of these boys and girls in a particular school depends partly on the willingness of teachers and administrators to accept such facts of life. Year by year, there are firmer indications from careful studies to show that more children rightly should be classified as hyperactive and/or perceptually handicapped than was suspected a short time ago. Good schools are trying to be aware of all children who have such difficulties.

This chapter has aimed largely to introduce the broad clinical aspects of these children. Following chapters will expand these facets in greater detail, with the hope of encouraging teachers and parents who read this book to join the bright quest for ways to help all such youngsters.

3

THESE BOYS AND GIRLS
ARE BEING HELPED . . .

The next decade will find good schools adapting and using new techniques and methods to help hyperactive children. Many teachers—and parents too—with an inventive flair and a desire to help such youngsters already are devising better classroom materials and methods. I have seen scores of teachers doing it in all kinds of school situations. There will always be children with a thousand variations of perceptual-motor difficulty who need special teaching methods. This is simply one of the facts of life.

The encouraging part of the picture is that we *can* find effective ways to help all these boys and girls. In fact, this kind of creative educational program is going ahead right now in good schools all around the world. You must have noticed at least a few of the signs of this progress:

——pertinent, down-to-earth articles in widely circulated magazines, on children who find school difficult and what parents and teachers can do to help.

——excellently portrayed TV programs about children with complex handicaps, and what community services can help these boys and girls.

——new child-and-family guidance centers that are opening or expanding, to offer professional consultation to parents as well as children.

——new trends in psychiatry that are inviting multidiscipline team-approaches to the intricate problems of diagnosis and treatment that jittery children present.

——expansion and upgrading of graduate level training and internship programs in special education, particularly for teachers who are working with children with minimal brain injury syndromes.

——increasing financial support for good special education services in our schools, plus increasing support for the research needed to make these services even more effective.

The most encouraging sign is that more teachers in more schools are becoming interested in *and alert to* children with subtle nervous system difficulties that can handicap school progress so much.

Discerning these boys and girls early enough—particularly in their preschool and elementary grade years—is not an easy task. In some cases the differentials can tax the best psychiatrist, neurologist, and psychologist. But good teachers are noticing these youngsters early enough to send them along in time to obtain the help they need when it can do the most good.

These children at least will not have to struggle as hard *with as many complicating emotional troubles* as other children who are brought in at later ages for such help. This change in the old picture takes time to catch up to some communities, yet it is spreading. Who could argue that this change is worthless, when many children are being greatly helped?

Increased awareness of children with milder degrees of cerebral dysfunction has been promoting extensive research on diagnostic instruments and techniques to discern these children more clearly. The usual neurological examination that used to be standard practice a decade ago with physicians simply was inadequate to spot many children with minimal brain damage. *Many youngsters with only slight cerebral dysfunction learn to accomodate quite well, and this can hide the real difficulty enough to escape notice in a gross examination.* Thoughtful physicians now take whatever extra time is needed, to check for fine perceptual-motor disturbances and disruptions. Asking the child to copy a geometric figure, or color and cut out a doll-figure, can spot subtle imperceptions in some children.

Careful research has been producing excellent psychological tests that are quite sensitive to perceptual-motor troubles in a child. These new instruments and techniques are rapidly being accepted in many child guidance centers as valuable diagnostic tools. Schools too, are beginning to utilize these instruments to check boys and girls who are having much difficulty in learning.

One important outcome of these changes—at least in some alert communities—is that fewer children are tagged now with the old labels that were based on ignorance of how the brain really functions. Good teachers are realizing that there are many children in any school with subtle brain electrochemical differences that do not clear up by commanding these youngsters to study harder or stop being jittery.

Better trained teachers now are aware that the old panaceas of *more work and less nonsense* are useless in helping boys and girls with much perceptual difficulty. These teachers know that the best help for such children lies largely in radically different kinds of classroom methods, as well as materials.

These teachers do not have to be psychologists or neurologists to do the job. This point is important to stress here. A thoughtful teacher with some experience with children having learning difficulties can develop the knowledge and skills needed to do an excellent job with the kinds of children we are discussing in this book. Of course the job takes the right determination, dedication, study, and effort, but it is a very rewarding job.

Good teachers are increasingly aware of possible organicity beneath the *emotional* picture in many children, especially those who show signals of perceptual trouble too. Extensive studies of such children, usually involving electroencephalographic evaluations as well as neuropsychological examinations, are pointing strongly to brain dysfunction in a large

40

percentage of the cases. Studies of available health records of such children have been providing evidence of linkage between childhood injuries and illnesses and later learning difficulties.

Further studies recently are pointing to inborn errors of metabolism and enzyme disturbances as major causes of development, behavior, and learning difficulties in many children who seem to be hysteric or borderline schizophrenic by nature. Heredity undoubtedly plays a part in the temperaments and personality traits we show—perhaps more than we have wanted to admit in the past few decades since the advent of believing such things are just matters of willing-them-to-be-so.

The picture is still not a gloomy one, however. *Many children who have suffered some kind of cerebral insult will grow up to become very capable and effective adults.* Injuries to the central nervous system and brain do not necessarily bring serious school trouble, or lead to rough behavior problems. Some children who sustained such injuries arrive at school years with imperceptible sequelae. Many factors in recovery are as yet only beginning to be guessed. There is little correlation between the extent and degree of cerebral injury and the apparent effects in behavior and intellectual abilities a few years later.

The time-lapse between the possible injury and the apparent effects in many cases has been puzzling the best researchers for a long time. Only recently has any real advance been made to answer this question. Even now the answers we do have are not crystal clear and positive. But we are gaining.

This decade still may disclose important information from several large group studies now going on, via the help of new electronic data-processing methods. Meanwhile, more studies of smaller groups of hyperactive children are supporting a firm relationship between jittery behavior, perceptual-language-motor trouble, and school failure quite like that seen so often in children with known brain injury.

One 10-year-old who had been quite a puzzle to his parents and teachers comes to mind. It would have been easy to mis-

41

judge Robert's real trouble; there were a dozen possibilities to blame the family first, and then the schools he had attended, and the neighborhood where he was living at the time. But there were some other facts too.

When the boy was nine and in third grade, he began to seem very irritable, and his spelling was poorer than it had been. His parents were urged to accept the boy better, criticize him less, value him more, and nag him less. These suggestions were tried and did help a little.

The family physician sent Robert for a thorough neurological checkup. Then clearer light began to shine on the problem. A special EEG hinted at cerebral dysfunction, perhaps stemming from an early injury. The parents said Robert had been convulsive around the age of two and a half to three.

At ten and in fourth grade, he showed complex perceptual and language difficulties. He could hardly manage reading at third grade level, and his reading comprehension was poorer still. Some days he was a disruptive youngster in the classroom.

This was fifteen years ago, before modern medications were available to help such children. Yet the anticonvulsive medication prescribed by the physician did help the boy greatly. The changes in his school behavior were enough to cheer the teacher and encourage the parents. Calmer, happier Robert improved in reading so much in two years that we wondered whether the tests had been accurate.

Much more mature now, Robert has a good job in construction, and two fine children who are coming along well in school. He has often talked about the old troubles he had in school when he was a boy. Part of the old trouble may simply have been that the boy was misjudged so long by teachers who should have sent him along for clearer diagnosis.

We are doing better now with such children, and there are good signs that many teachers in many school systems are catching the idea of how to help. Important progress has been happening.

42

Caton, in 1875 in England, was demonstrating electrical activity in the living brains of animals in his laboratory. This was a great stride forward in such knowledge. But more than half a century was to pass before the next great advance in 1935, when Hans Berger published his first recordings of electrical activity in the human brain.

This remarkable breakthrough brought swift successions of electroencephalographic techniques and instruments. Our present decade is seeing marvelous advances in this field, coupled with parallel strides in biochemistry, neurosurgery, psychiatry, and electronics. New cooperation between these fields is opening hope of remediation and even cure for many brain-injured children.

Perhaps not far ahead we will be utilizing scores of yet unknown techniques to help these children. Teachers who are alert to the signs of such children have an important part in this needed advance.

Many scientist-engineers in electronics are busy devising better instruments to record and analyze brain-current patterns. These new devices, in the hands of specialists in neurology, are heralding an era of better understanding *and treatment* for children who show behavior and learning problems.

EEG evaluation still finds only about half of these children, but the newest instruments already are enhancing the possibilities in this field. The EEG tracings of two 12-year-olds reproduced on the next page intimate some of the breakthroughs not far ahead.

Especially since 1930, a host of studies have been accumulating around the clinical implications of encephalographic observations of children with complex school difficulties. The high quality of these researches has deserved far better attention than many of them have received. The renewed insight and interest about organic bases of behavioral difficulties is bringing wider discussion of such matters. Some of the old biases are gradually dwindling in clinical circles. All this is good.

Electroencephalograms* of two 12-year-olds:

Roslynn is a rather *calm and collected* youngster, getting along in school quite well, with no real behavior problems in school or at home. Her mother says the girl has never seemed very jittery or nervous. The pregnancy and birth were without complications. The left parietal area wave tracing is shown

here; the tracings from other cortical areas were similar. There were no electrical signs in her EEG record that might point to abnormal brain function. The recorded voltages (amplitude) and frequencies were within the ranges for children with no demonstrable brain dysfunction or injury.

Cheryl is just as attractive as Roslynn, but she frequently seems very upset and jittery, with many *irritable days* that are difficult to trace to happenings

around her in school or at home. Medication has helped somewhat, but she still complains of stormy feelings at times. This section of the EEG record was typical of the whole record. Notice the increased voltages and the much slower and faster waves, with many sharp spikes.

Both these girls are above average in intellectual potentials, yet Cheryl is having great trouble in passing, while Roslynn sails through with little apparent effort. When Cheryl was five, she sustained a severe head injury that was followed by convulsions.

*Chapter 11 discusses problems of EEG interpretation in greater detail.

Electroencephalographic observation is a valuable tool with every child who shows extensive school difficulties. By itself, the EEG can hardly substitute for high level experience and skill in diagnosis and therapy. Such instruments, marvelous as they are, still were never intended to be more than instruments. Yet in the hands of experts, the EEG has become a valued tool in diagnosis and treatment of children with learning difficulties and behavior problems. The last forty years has seen steep changes in its acceptance and use.

In 1935, Jasper along with Solomon and Bradley already were reporting an intensive electroencephalographic analysis of children with severe behavioral and thinking difficulties. One group of seventy-one of these children were carefully matched with another group of children who had no difficulties. Nearly three-fourths of the behavioral group produced EEG tracings that pointed definitely to organic bases of the surface troubles. Few control children showed such signs.

By 1940, Lindsley and Cutts were reporting parallel findings from exacting studies on children diagnosed as "constitutionally inferior" and as "behavior disorders." These two groups of children had EEG tracings showing organic abnormality in a high percentage of the cases. Normal children in the control groups showed no pathologic variations in their EEG tracings.

At the same time, Hans Strauss, with Rahm and Barrera, were hard at work with children from three to twelve who are suffering from various psychiatric disorders. Only nine of these forty-four children were found to have EEG tracings that could be considered within normal variations. Another research team—Brill, Seideman, Montague, and Balser—reported studies of twenty-eight children from New York City's Domestic Relations Court. The children in this group who had single offenses of slight degree or were simply in care as neglected children showed normal electroencephalograms. All the children with behavior disorders or psychotic behavior showed EEG abnormalities.

In still another study, Brown and Solomon reported on

twenty boys in a school for delinquent children. Seventeen of the twenty showed dysrhythmia in the EEG. This study further indicated that all the boys who were given Dilantin showed marked improvement in general behavior. Secunda and Findley, studying 143 children with severe behavior disorders, noted that only in eighteen per cent of the cases were the EEG tracings within normal variation range. In the control group of children, sixty-eight per cent were, without doubt, normal in their EEG records.

One study was of particular interest partly because the researchers — Solomon, Brown, and Deutscher — had hoped to *disprove* any relationship between EEG findings and behavior disorders in children. This team studied forty children from a junior high and twenty from a special school for delinquent boys. These groups then were classified into two sections: best behaved and worst behaved. The poorest-behaving section of the delinquent group had ninety per cent of the abnormal EEG tracings. There was solid evidence of high relationship between abnormal EEG tracings and serious behavior disorders in these boys.

By 1958, Margaret Kennard was reporting high correlation between electroencephalographic abnormality and marked thought disorder in children. Robert Cohn and J. E. Nardini reported abnormal slow EEG activity in the occipital area of children with behavior abnormality.

The possibility that physical abnormality of the brain—at least of cortical areas of the brain, as reflected by electrical recording—is correlated with psychological abnormality, as reflected in human behavior difficulties, must now be considered to have a firm tradition out of such research data.

A point worth noting here is that chronic brain syndromes always show a preponderance of abnormal *stormy* EEG tracings, reflecting the stormy undercurrent in these children. Children diagnosed as "personality disorders" frequently show disproportionately high pathologic tracings. This has been true in every careful study of EEG's in children with behavior problems and/or psychotic reactions. The tendency toward gross abnormality in the tracings is somewhat lower than in children with severe motor involvement, but it is still high.

New EEG techniques—employing small doses of pentothal at a subanesthetic level—are improving diagnostic efficiency with many children. Clearer differential diagnosis, between cerebral dysfunction and psychotic illness, is more and more attainable now through the aid of modern EEG instruments. Better treatment is coming in these cases, aimed more effectively at deeper neuro-psychiatric difficulties. Just a few years ahead, there may be radically improved treatment in many cases that have seemed so resistive to the old methods.

A very hopeful factor has been rising out of extensive researches into children's EEG tracings across several years: *Apparently there are strong growth forces in every child, brain-injured or intact, that can be assisted by suitable care and treatment.* Good pharmacologic treatment is becoming an increasing part of this hopeful picture. So are the new and effective repatterning and relearning educational therapies. The development of the modern EEG and tracing analyzer instruments have had a large part in these important advances.

H. W. Newell in 1935 reported his study of the intricate effects of slight head injuries on the personality and behavior of some children. Twenty such cases had come to his attention. Newell's findings on this group of boys and girls have led to further researches since then that have substantiated his early data.

The most frequent sequelae that he noted that have been found in subsequent studies of cranial trauma in children include *an increase in general irritability* accompanied by *a general decrease in self-control.* These children seem markedly touchier and crankier than others who have not been injured, with considerably less ability to manage their impulses.

Ten of the children in his group showed "neurotic" symptoms following head injury. Five became involved in "delinquent" behavior. About the same time, Rylander was carefully evalu-

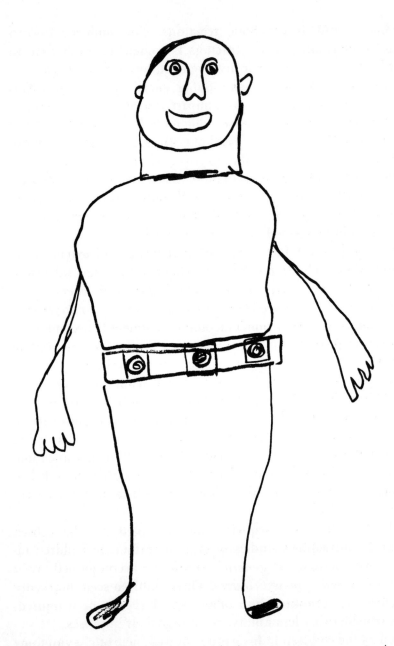

This 11-year-old's drawing of a man, plus his best attempt to copy a simple design, give many indications of a complex mixture of organicity overlaid with emotional disturbances.

Such a youngster usually is obvious in the group, and would hardly be thought to be normal.

This boy said he often felt useless and not like other boys in the school. By fifteen he still was unable to read above primer level.

Birth records included a note of oxygen shortage, but no other difficulty. At two he had sustained a severe head injury in a fall down the stairs.

the design . . .

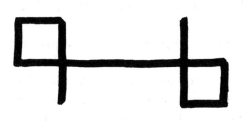

his best copy . . .

ating personality changes in thirty-two children on whom operations had been performed in the hope of clearing some of their difficulties which were felt to have started in the frontal brain lobes.

In twenty-one of these children, Rylander found intellectual reductions. Greatly diminished inhibition of affective responses was found in twenty-five of the group. In twenty-two, marked alterations occurred in volitional power. Brain injury in these children had apparently brought many personality and behavior changes.

Since these earlier studies, many others have been supporting the idea that cerebral injury sometimes incurs diffuse changes in a child's outer behavior and personality aspects. This should not be surprising to anyone who understands the foundations of intellect and behavior in the central nervous system and brain.

Children's drawings frequently offer excellent insight into personality dynamics and peculiarities. The clinician must, of course, be expertly trained in such techniques to utilize them accurately. But a thoughtful teacher can often catch glimpses of many inner facets of a child by studying the youngster's drawings. An intimate knowledge of the child's accepted ways of life at home and in his own community are necessary here, to avoid incorrect interpretation of a particular drawing a child may offer.

Children growing up in the Iatmul tribe, in New Guinea, for example, draw figures quite different in form and action than children growing up in the Sajan tribe, on Bali. In fact, children in Manhattan's crowded areas draw people differently than do children from Minnesota's wide farmlands. You would expect a Japanese child to draw people's faces with Oriental expressions.

Yet an experienced teacher who has been studying children's drawings of themselves for a while can recognize many signals of trouble with perception and self-image in such drawings. Nearly any thoughtful teacher or parent can surmise some of the differences between the children who drew the figures on the next pages. One child was a happy boy, getting along quite well in school and around his neighborhood. The other boy was a very difficult youngster to manage much of the time in school and at home.

If these two boys were in your class and you were to be their teacher, which boy would you think (from his drawing of a man for you) might be:

——calmer and less disturbed by extraneous stimuli

——easier to get settled down to good work

——more self-confident in the group

——better able to distinguish reality from fantasy

——less apt to be perceptually confused

——freer from jittery feelings

——generally more mature and capable

The boy who drew the figure with bizarre features was later diagnosed as brain-injured. Continuing medical therapy has helped him come to adolescence much calmer and happier than he used to be. His parents needed wise support for a long time as the boy changed slowly toward better behavior. Many times they were very discouraged, but have never completely lost hope that the picture will be better someday. They have always loved this boy very much, and he has always seemed to know this. In my private case files there are 35-mm color slides of this boy working hard on special tests when he was about ten. If you saw these pictures on the screen and just looked at his face, you would never guess he was such a problem child at times. I used to marvel at his mother's enduring love for the boy, no matter how naughty he seemed to others.

Children who sustained brain injuries sometimes behave in ways that would make them seem a little schizophrenic, if the health history was incomplete or not available for study in these cases.

The differentials between children who are behaving as they do because of subtle brain injury (hyperkinetic syndrome children), and other children who are reacting as they do more

Two 8-year-old boys drew a man . . .

The boy who drew this figure was getting along well in grade 3, and had no trouble with schoolwork. His mother reported no behavior difficulties at home. "He gets along all right, we've had no trouble with him. . . ."

The boy who drew this figure had been diagnosed as probably schizophrenic. He scribbled the upper body first, then built the figure around it. The kind of lag noticeable in this figure has a bizarreness about it that is reflective of something more than simple deficiency or even of subtle brain injury. As he got older, he lost much of the early emotional signals although he is still jittery at times. His reading level is quite good—for him.

". . . there's a truck running inside me, makes me mad about the noise."

because of schizophrenic disturbances, still reveal *possible deeper organicities common to both groups.*

Some children who show perceptual difficulties are not obviously jittery or hyperactive. Other children with perceptual difficulties may seem quite schizophrenic at times. The differentials in a particular child sometimes are so clouded and overlapping that sharp diagnosis would be hard to make.

Neurology and psychiatry are not yet sufficiently refined to provide completely clear answers about some children who are having much trouble in life. The emotional overlay in a child who has felt very upset and discouraged a long time can mask primary organicity so that it seems to be only secondary as a cause of the behavior abnormality.

New techniques in clinical psychology are helping a little in these diagnostic puzzles, but even these test instruments require expert knowledge and experience to use them wisely in any case. This is no field for inexperienced persons.

Research findings on the possibility of children inheriting schizophrenic tendencies are interesting. Studies show as high as seventy per cent of such children have at least one parent with clinically discernable disorders of conceptual thinking. Only one per cent of children deemed normal have a parent with such a thought disorder. This difference is great enough to point to hereditary transmission of schizophrenic tendencies.

This, of course, still does not prevent schizophrenic disorders from happening in some children because of electrochemical cellular dysfunctions that as yet are barely suspicioned. The kinds of perceptual-motor dysfunction discussed in these chapters seem to involve no strong hereditary factors. At least none has been discovered thus far in studies that have been done.

Children who show even a portion of the clinical picture of perceptual-motor disturbances can pose complex school problems at any grade level. When these boys and girls seem to *come unglued* in jittery behavior spells, the situation can upset parents as well as teachers.

There are no sure-to-cure remedies. There are, however,

some broad prescriptions that help with many children who feel jittery and unable to settle down to work. The catalytic agents in any of these prescriptions include the teacher's warmth of personality and wisdom about life.

Cerebral injury in a child does not rule out a hopeful prognosis. Many jittery, hyperactive boys and girls with perceptual-motor handicaps—with or without demonstrable brain injury—have shown good progress in the right learning situations at home, as well as in school. There is no reason to write off such a boy or girl as not worth the effort to try to help him overcome his handicaps.

One of the marks of thoughtful teachers in every good school is that they are inclined to look at each child hopefully. They are inclined to see him in the bright light of whatever facts are available about him, and do not submerge these facts under mushy sentiment about the child. Thoughtful teachers are able to comprehend these facts in the light of intelligent hope too. Most children are likely to do better in such a climate.

The prognosis in the case of a child who may have sustained brain injury depends, of course, on several factors each of which can be very important. These factors are:

The child's innate intellectual endowment—The brighter and more capable and resilient he is by nature, the better he probably can learn to manage, and even overcome, the effects of the injury.

The extent and severity of the injury or dysfunction—Minimal injury to some cortical or subcortical areas may have much less effect on intellective powers and general behavior than severe and diffuse injury to other areas, particularly in the dominant hemisphere.

The nature of the offending agent and circumstances—Preston found that the overall prognosis was good in children with behavior disorders that were primarily associated with anoxic damage to the brain, especially if diagnosis was made early and proper treatment instituted.

The emotional and reeducational support the child receives—
The dominating drive in very jittery youngsters, no matter what the cause, still is toward better health and development, quite as in children who feel well and calm. Every child wants to attain fullest stature of personality and spirit, as well as of body. Here is a life force amazingly capable of overcoming great obstacles.

Careful followup studies of such children have been showing that the prognosis is better when diagnosis is made early, and the right treatment is put in operation promptly and kept in operation long enough.

Parents take hope better when they have warm support and encouragement that is based on honesty. The truth, at least as nearly as we can discern it, sets us free from morbid fears and needless anxiety, so that we can begin to do what can be done in a particular situation.

Teachers who have come to realize that the jittery child's behavior often stems from a defect for which the youngster is not responsible yet has to bear somehow, can greatly help the parents. This task requires maturity of spirit and wisdom about life, but good teachers have enough of these characteristics to do the job in most instances. I have seen a hundred good teachers do it. I have seen parents who were disheartened about a child manage to do it. What often helped most were conferences with good teachers who encouraged new insight and realistic hope about the same children who had previously been "terrible problems."

And in a few months, the children were changing, too. No miracle was happening—unless you can concede that clearer insight, better self-understanding and acceptance, and renewed courage and hope always are miracles. I have long thought they are the greatest miracles, because they are so marvelously available to us when we reach out to grasp them.

Brief syntheses of any complex technique can make things that still are very difficult seem simple. Oversimplification always brings such a risk. Yet this may be an appropriate place in such a discussion of jittery children to present two under-girding principles that form a good foundation for helping such youngsters. As the parent or teacher, you can help the child more effectively if you:

come to understand the child a little clearer day by day, see-ing him as a whole child with some problems in living that you can help him circumvent or manage.

keep a warm, durable patience toward yourself, so you are not discouraged when your plans for the youngster do not show great dividends in a few days or weeks—or even months. With this kind of resilient patience and inner-confidence about yourself, you can afford to try a hundred new ideas, some of which will work!

Such a viewpoint enables any helpful teacher (or parent) to tackle the job of trying to help practically any child, no mat-ter how jittery and perceptually handicapped he has been. Ac-tually, in many cases, the *clinical clues about the child* pro-vide very practical *cues about what to do to help him.* Hungry youngsters obviously need to be fed. Certainly children who have felt very discouraged need warm, genuine encouragement. Children who have been tumbling downhill secretly in self-value greatly need the right kind of help to regain healthy self-esteem.

While such inner changes really are part of the primary aims of an effective program for jittery children, they usually are attained *as outgrowths of therapy that has been planned to relieve and counteract more specific symptoms in the partic-ular child.*

As a case in point here, suppose a child is so hyperactive and excitable in the classroom that he seems unable to sit still long enough to do anything sensible. Perhaps his top need is to have the right chemotherapeutic help just to be a little calm-er. Some very jittery children have responded almost miracu-lously to the right drugs.

Yet drugs should not be relied upon as the sole therapeutic approach in most cases. The best drugs available may still fail to remedy some of the underlying causes of the child's outward behavior. Many effective drugs do have rightful uses in the therapy program with particular children who, at least for a while, need this extra help in building better behavior patterns. Scores of children with subtle brain injuries have been able to establish much happier general attitudes and behavior with the partial help of the right drugs wisely prescribed by the family physician.

One mother had felt so hopeless about her very hyperactive 8-year-old that she had been trying to find a special boarding school for the boy. Her own nerves were frazzled at the end of the usual day with the child. The father thought the boy just needed "tighter controls at home and in school." A conference with the parents helped them decide to ask the family physician to look at the boy carefully. The examination brought several neurological signs to light, and the physician prescribed one of the new amphetamine derivitives on a trial basis. The change in the boy in the next few weeks was amazing. He became much calmer, less explosive, and had fewer angry outbursts when his younger brother annoyed him or when things did not please him in school. Other children began to like to have him with them.

Children who feel calmer and are not as distractable usually do better on so-called IQ tests. It is not surprising, then, to find good changes in test scores with children who are on mild chemotherapy for jitteriness. I can recall many instances when apparent IQ scores went up as much as twenty points in a few months. There still were clinical signs of neurological difficulty in many of these children, but their overall test performances— and school marks—had increased encouragingly.

Many jittery children have improved to show less aggressiveness, fearfulness, anxiety, sexual tension, and hyperactivity, with the help of the right drugs. They become a little calmer, not as noisy, and not as easily tipped into the old rages. Parents as well as teachers appreciate these changes in any youngster.

But even more important, the children begin to feel better about themselves; less anxious, and a little surer of themselves. One 11-year-old said, "Now I am beginning to like myself, and it's a good feeling. I used to wish I could disappear completely, or turn into another person . . . ."

These changes in the child's personality and behavior bring many healthy changes in parents, and in teachers too. Nagging, scolding, and threatening decrease. The old need for bargaining and haranguing subsides. One mother confided, "Janet and I went shopping together yesterday, and I was so happy about the way she behaved. I can hardly believe she used to be so hard to control and threw such tantrums." This girl has since graduated from high school, and works in the cafeteria of a large hospital. Yet when the girl was ten, the teacher used to wonder whether the girl would ever reach fifth grade.

When a child feels calm enough, he often can do things that seemed completely beyond him when he was very jittery and upset. Nobody can learn very well when *wound up;* we just are not geared that way. Have you ever tried to do something very important—like phrasing a special paragraph in words that will put across exactly what you really want to say—when you were very tense or disturbed? If you were able to do the job at all, it probably turned out far from your best level. Imagine trying to do a beautiful wallpapering job, or attempting to compose a symphony when you secretly felt terribly discouraged and hopeless about yourself.

A fair degree of inner calm and freedom from confusion is necessary before we can be creative. Little wonder then that jittery children rarely seem creative, even when they are very bright.

Younger hyperactive children are not aware they are so distractible and so jumpy. Robert, a very hyperactive boy who had sustained diffuse brain injury at birth, was nearly twelve when he finally said one day, "Now I can tell sometimes when I feel very loop-the-loopy inside me, and sometimes I can make myself quiet down a little, but it sure is hard to do." He was just beginning to get a toehold on first-grade reading, yet on some of the WISC subscales he rated above average in intelligence. He still was having days when he seemed practically unable to manage vague restlessness, bending, stretching, and even whirling around the room at times. These clinical signs reflected subcortical as well as cortical disturbances quite beyond much voluntary control. His self-description of feeling very loop-the-loopy at times seemed an accurate diagnosis to me. He often seemed to be in tailspins and sideslips, like a plane out of control.

Teaching these children how to help themselves become a little less unglued and jittery is not an easy job, but it can be done. The teaching secret is not one of harsh discipline imposed by force on the child, but almost the opposite. The child probably has never really noticed how fragmented he has been. Many hyperactive adolescents think their calmer chums are just pepless or not interested in *doing things.* "Who says she's nervous? Maybe she has trouble sitting still in some classes, but this doesn't mean her nerves are bad, does it?" one mother asked seriously about her 14-year-old daughter. It was not easy to persuade this mother to look a little more closely at the clinical picture. Two years later, she said she was glad I had urged her to read the book on minimally brain-injured children.

Supporting *and encouraging* the parent in such cases is an integral part in helping these children. This is not easy to remember at times. I know from experience. Yet the right support and encouragement for the parent can be even more important than directly trying to help the child himself.

Any boy or girl who has been living in a discordant home where nagging is common can hardly feel much like trying to *do better in school.* Few of us feel like doing the best we can when those who ought to love and value us reflect chronic disappointment with us.

One touchy 12-year-old put it plainly enough. "My father

says I won't amount to much anyway. If I have to have the name, I might as well have the fame." The next report period, this lad turned up with all failing marks.

The father was really not a bad father. He did have considerable hope about the boy, though he had not taken time to say so in ordinary words or actions. The teacher was instrumental in helping the man see this point and change the picture for the better in the next few months. Then the boy made some remarkable strides too, particularly in his general behavior at home.

4

THE BEST CATALYZER
STILL IS A
GOOD TEACHER . . .

The teacher who is warmly outgoing toward all children is veritably worth his or her brain-weight in jewels! Such a teacher can give a jittery and sensitive child a feeling of being accepted, no matter what the impediment or handicap. The youngster generates a feeling of belonging, of being valued for what he is right now, as well as what he may become with the right effort and courage.

Invisibly handicapped children can feel just as unhappy and uncared for as children with obvious handicaps. Children always know when they are unable to do as well as other boys and girls. This self-knowledge swiftly depletes courage, hope, and desire to keep trying. Here a wise and thoughtful teacher becomes priceless, in helping the child circumvent chronic failure.

Perceptually handicapped youngsters usually show general motor disturbances and dysfunctions too. Hence the hyphenated term *perceptual-motor-language difficulty* now commonly applied to such cases in modern psychological and neurological literature. Yet many teachers and parents overlook this close relationship in a jittery child, and often expect him to do fairly well in shop, gym, and art, eventhough he has so much trouble in reading, spelling, and arithmetic. We need to remember that the same brain and central nervous system directs all the child's activities and behavior.

All teachers need to be alert to signals of possible organicity in children. The youngster who has peculiar difficulty in duplicating simple geometric figures, for example, probably is finding trouble in spelling, number concepts, understanding a drawing in shop, or fitting a dress pattern to the cloth in the best way in homemaking. The degree of difficulty depends somewhat on the extent of the cerebral dysfunction, of course, as well as on how the child feels about the situation.

This is no surprise to teachers who have worked with boys and girls with the kinds of perceptual-motor involvements we are discussing in this book. Such children, whether or not they show frank signs of brain injury, are apt to need special help with school tasks that require:
——steady, calm attention to specific details.
——ability to differentiate figure-motive from background.
——accurate retention of complex data.
——excellent control of muscle systems.
——well coordinated eye-hand movements.
——clear perception and ability to apply concepts and rules.
——inner poise and equilibrium—freedom from excessive tension and anxiety, so that minor difficulties do not swiftly bring discouragement.

That so many children who feel jittery and inept still come to school every morning with renewed courage and hope about themselves has amazed and cheered me for years. Our boys and girls apparently have an in-built ruggedness of spirit that makes me firmly believe that we are created to overcome great obstacles. Our potentials often far exceed our efforts and achievements.

The mature and wise teacher can perceive the major dimensions of these *potentials* in a child, yet not lose sight of the youngster's handicaps and organic limitations. This teacher stands in a marvelous place of power in the picture, and can help the child to grow to help himself in the best ways. This

Kathy was ten before she was able to reproduce this figure of an overlapping diamond and square as well as shown below. The task took her five times as long as other children, who have no perceptual-motor trouble, usually need.

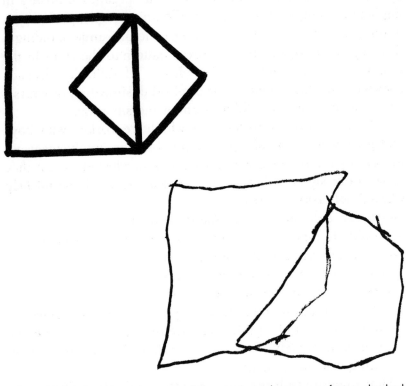

It is not hard to imagine some of the perceptual-motor confusion she had been facing in earlier grades. Perhaps the severe measles infection she suffered when she was about 3-years-old was the cause of the later school difficulties she showed. The family physician felt this had been the cause.

When Kathy was ten, her parents agreed to let the school place her in a special class with an excellent teacher who knew how to help such children. Her reading then was very poor, barely up to grade 2.0 level. In three years, the girl was able to read much better, about grade 5 level. This was an amazing accomplishment, the teacher felt. Kathy's scores on the WISC reflected at least average intellectual potentials that were hampered by possible organic brain damage. She had never been much of an emotional problem, at home or in school, though the teachers said the child always had seemed "quite nervous."

is the true meaning of education: the art of drawing out and developing the child's best talents and capacities, so he comes to his fullest stature of spirit. Any teacher who is doing this is priceless, for this art cannot really be bought anywhere for dollars.

Expecting a child to start to read before *he* is ready, neurologically as well as emotionally, to manage such a task is unrealistic and harmful to the whole learning situation. To say the child is failing simply because he is not ready for the task, defeats and disrupts his wellsprings of courage and hope.

Part of the school's rightful job—and privilege—is to be expert in recognizing all children who seem headed for much learning trouble, and helping these children find better ways of becoming ready. Even if parents were not taxpayers, they have a right to expect such help from the school, simply because every child in every community is precious.

Teachers who are experimentally-minded, and who are inclined somewhat by nature to be innovators, seem better equipped to work well with children who feel very tense. These teachers are able to take tips from a hundred sources and apply them with happy results to the job of helping nervous, jumpy, *inattentive* youngsters want to be a little calmer, and try a little harder to learn.

These teachers are easy to interest in new books about such children and how to help them learn better. Children in these classrooms seem to sense the healthy atmosphere of warm hope and encouragement. Rough discipline situations do not often flare up in these classrooms.

In any prescription for helping jittery children in school, the warmth and sheer wisdom of the teacher have always been potent and invaluable factors. Take any mature teacher who shows open and wise understanding toward all children; add pertinent up-to-date psychologic and neurologic insight into children who may be brain-injured, then give this teacher healthy latitude to run a classroom for such children, and the project will be successful. A thousand happy, effective programs for these boys and girls in as many communities across the country are plain proof of this fact. I have seen many *ordinary* teachers with steady warmth of heart, earthy wisdom about life and the real world, *plus a high drive to learn how to help children with complex school problems,* do a surprisingly good job in such programs.

For teachers who have these characteristics, the job is wonderfully challenging. The special satisfactions in working with perceptually handicapped children far outweigh the investment in time and effort to learn to do the job well.

Many excellent texts have been published in recent years pertaining to children with subtle anomalies of the brain and central nervous system. Alert teachers have been studying these new texts, to keep abreast of important research findings and applications of neuropsychiatry to the classroom. Here are some of the books that many teachers I know have found invaluable in working with youngsters who often seem jittery and perceptually disturbed. I warmly recommend these texts to all teachers who care about such children. Copies can be borrowed from most up-to-date college or university libraries:

*Bakwin, H. and R., *Clinical Management of Behavior Disorders in Children.* Philadelphia: W.B. Saunders Company, 1954.

Bender, L., *Psychopathology of Children With Organic Brain Disorders.* Springfield, Ill.: Charles C. Thomas, Publisher, 1955.

Brain, R., *Speech Disorders: Aphasia, Apraxia, and Agnosia.* London: Butterworth & Co. (Publishers), Ltd., 1961.

*Burgemeister, B.B., *Psychological Techniques in Neurological Diagnosis.* New York: Harper & Row, Publishers, 1962.

*Chess, S., Thomas, A., and Birch, H., *Your Child Is a Person.* New York: The Viking Press, Inc., 1965.

*Cruikshank, W.M., and others, *A Teaching Method With Brain-Injured and Hyperactive Children.* Syracuse: Syracuse University Press, 1961.

Idem, Bice, H.V., and Wallen, N.E., *Perception and Cerebral Palsy.* Syracuse: Syracuse University Press, 1957.

*Asterisks indicate references that may be most helpful to less-experienced teachers who are interested in working with children who seem jittery and anxious.

*D'Evelyn, K.E., *Meeting Children's Emotional Needs*. Englewood Cliffs, N.J.: Prentice-Hall, Inc., 1957.

*Flanigan, G.L., *The First Nine Months of Life*. New York: Simon and Schuster, Inc., 1962.

Gettz, S.B., and Rees, E.L., *The Mentally Ill Child*. Springfield, Ill.: Charles C. Thomas, Publisher, 1957.

Harris, D.B., *Children's Drawings as Measures of Intellectual Maturity*. New York: Harcourt, Brace & World, Inc., 1963.

Holt, J., *How Children Fail*. New York: Pitman Publishing Corporation, 1964.

Cerebral Mechanisms in Behavior, L. A. Jefferies, ed. New York: John Wiley & Sons, Inc., 1951.

Keller, H., *The Story of My Life*. New York: Doubleday & Company, Inc., 1931.

*Kephart, N.C., *The Slow-Learner in the Classroom*. Springfield, Ill.: Charles C. Thomas, Publisher, 1960.

*Kimble, D.D., *Physiological Psychology*. Reading, Mass.: Addison-Wesley Publishing Company, Inc., 1963.

*Kirk, S. A., *Educating Exceptional Children*. Boston: Houghton Mifflin Company, 1962.

Klein, R., and Mayer-Gross, W., *Clinical Examination of Children With Organic Brain Disease*. Springfield, Ill.: Charles C. Thomas, Publisher, 1957.

Leibman, S., *Emotional Problems of Childhood*. Philadelphia: J.B. Lippincott Company, 1958.

Lippman, H.S., *Treatment of the Child in Emotional Conflict*. New York: McGraw-Hill, Inc., 1962.

Livingston, S., *Diagnosis and Treatment of Convulsive Disorders in Children*. Springfield, Ill.: Charles C. Thomas, Publisher, 1954.

Parkhurst, H., *Exploring the Child's Mind*. New York: Appleton-Century-Crofts, 1955.

Penfield, W., and Roberts, L., *Speech and Brain Mechanisms*. Princeton: Princeton University Press, 1959.

Idem, and Rasmussen, T., *The Cerebral Cortex of Man*. New York: The Macmillan Company, 1950.

*Roswell, F., and Natchez, G., *Reading Disability: Diagnosis and Treatment*. New York: Basic Books, Inc., 1964.

*Sarason, S., and others, *Anxiety in Elementary School Children*. New York: John Wiley & Sons, Inc., 1960.

Schilder, P., *Image and Appearance of the Human Body*. New York: International Universities Press, Inc., 1951.

*Strauss, A.A., and Lehtinen, L.E., *Psychopathology and Education of the Brain-Injured Child*. New York: Grune & Stratton, Inc., 1950. Vol. I and II.

These texts are among the classics in this important field, representing the breakthrough that had been coming since Hippocrates, circa 300 B.C.

Bill is an attractive 11-year-old who is floundering in grade 5. Careful examination of the boy and extensive talks with his parents have revealed no emotional disturbances in Bill that could really account for the trouble he has in reading, spelling, and arithmetic.

You would not have to be around Bill very long to be sure he is not mentally deficient. And yet he found great difficulty in reproducing some of the Taylor-Dobson designs from memory. The subtle brain injury that Bill sustained has largely cleared, but it still handicaps him *perceptually*. He needed five minutes to write this for me (Help me learn to write a little better):

68% actual size

68

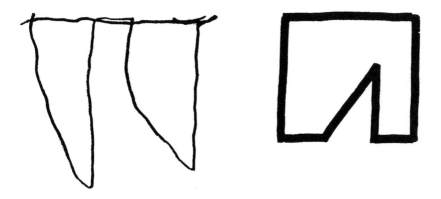

Will he ever be much better than he seemed then? I am always hopeful about such matters, but in recent years I have been cautious in guessing ahead too far.

In this boy's case, I encouraged the teacher not to worry much about spelling. The boy may never spell well, even though he is quite intelligent in many other ways.

*Taylor, E.M., *Psychological Appraisal of Children With Cerebral Defects.* Cambridge, Mass.: Harvard University Press, 1961.

Vernon, M.D., *A Further Study of Visual Perception.* Cambridge: Cambridge University Press, 1952.

*Idem, *Backwardness in Reading.* Cambridge: Cambridge University Press, 1957.

Walter, W.G., *The Living Brain.* New York: W.W. Norton & Company, Inc., 1953.

Wepman, J.M., *Recovery From Aphasia.* New York: The Ronald Press Company, 1951.

Recently several excellent books are coming into use for art teachers who are trying to help children with subtle perceptual-motor difficulties. Newell Kephart certainly widened this educational highway by his own text on *The Slow Learner in the Classroom,* noted in the brief list above. Good teachers will benefit greatly by thoughtfully reading the books listed, especially Kephart, Cruikshank, and Kirk.

For inventive-minded teachers with even a slight flair for art, many of the new books in this field can supply bases for scores of interesting projects that will also be therapeutic for children who need to develop better perception and better eye-motor coordination. Such *resource books* I have found invaluable to teachers who already understand the implications of organicity in children. Several of my teacher friends who work with the kind of children we have been discussing in these chapters are finding these books on the special creative play series valuable adjuncts:

Creative Drawing by Ernst Rottger, and Dieter Klante
Creative Paper Sculpture by Ernst Rottger
Creative Wood Design by Ernst Rottger
Creative Clay Design by Ernst Rottger
Creative Textile Design by Ralph Hartung

These are all published by Reinhold Publishing Corporation, New York.

There have always been boys and girls like Bill. There will be many more like him who will be coming to our schools,

70

just as other children now come. Scolding and failing these children will not meet the challenge they present. What will help these boys and girls certainly includes:

——teachers' *early* recognition of the signals

——prompt referral for psychological study (neurological also if needed)

——bringing forward the best modern resources and techniques to enable the child to circumvent the handicap in effective ways, while he learns to live intelligently with whatever facets of the problem cannot really be changed

Every child is worth this investment of plans and programs. Good teachers have always been in the vanguard of the people who are able to find ways to help children having complex learning difficulties. Of course this task takes a warm mixture of ingenuity and initiative, but these qualities have always been marks of a good teacher. I have seen a thousand children come to new courage and hope about themselves, under the care of such teachers.

When a teacher finds enthusiastic support and cooperation as a team member with the principal, psychologist, nurse, counselor, and school physician, whole communities can begin to do great things for children, with parents working hard at the tasks, too.

A good teacher can be a wonderful catalyzer, in any school.

5

ALERT TEACHERS
CAN DISCERN
THE SIGNALS . . .

Experienced teachers, especially those who inherently like children, are in a strategic position to spot youngsters who need help, early. Good teachers know that the best help depends partly on early recognition of the real difffculty, before a child becomes very discouraged.

Children with severe perceptual-language-motor dysfunctions usually present so many frank school problems that teachers soon call for the psychologist and anyone else who might relieve the situation. Calling for whatever help is available in these cases is a mark of a wise teacher and quite commendable.

Just as wise and commendable are teachers who call early for expert consultation and help about children who show only *mild* signs of such trouble. There are many children in this category, sometimes as high as one in five in a classroom. They have to face subtle organic dysfunctions and disturbances that still can greatly frustrate and discourage. These boys and girls need to be found early enough too, and afforded the very best help that is available.

Here is where alert teachers who are gaining skill in spotting such children early are multiplying the value of the school psychologist a hundredfold. So welcome aboard, there is a big job to be done.

Much as in all therapy arts, the child's feeling of being valued and secure in the teacher's attitude is critically important in any diagnostic situation too. Testing and remedial relationships with the child especially need his best cooperation and rapport, and are dependent on mutual trust and respect. Jittery and discouraged youngsters who are sent along for testing because they have been such problems in class are apt to feel in even greater jeopardy and react to this anxiety.

Children are swift to sense our deeper feelings toward them, and they respond similarly. Blessing the child that you are trying to help in your own heart has seemingly magic power over scolding him. It is not magic, but the soundest of applied psychology.

Hopeful teachers are inclined to be more helpful teachers, open to innovations and adaptations of techniques that often bring surprising success where other methods failed. Hopeful teachers who like to improvise and experiment with new ideas and possibilities *are* gifted teachers. Handicapped children's extra needs do not upset or baffle such teachers, but challenge them to more inventions and adaptations that may work. All children like hopeful teachers.

These are the teachers who can utilize such clinical suggestions as follow, to boost their insight about children who may have perceptual-motor handicaps that have been interfering with learning. This part of the book is not aimed to make good teachers into clinical psychologists and diagnosticians, but simply aims to make them better teachers.

The clinical tests suggested below are neuropsychological in nature, intended to elicit some signs of perceptual-motor dysfunction or difficulty. The child need not be aware of this. He probably will respond better, in any case, if he understands that the tests are simply part of the teacher's methods of discovering how best to help every child in the class who has been finding difficulty with schoolwork. With this kind of warm rapport, these tests should not make the child feel anxious or in danger.

Teacher's general impression of the child

Reviewing the child's behavior in the class group, as well as when he is alone, may reveal many clinically significant signals of feeling very tense, often involving perceptual difficulties that have been handicapping full learning.

Children with possible subtle brain lesions often show a broad scatter of signs that are not confined to one area of behavior. This is not surprising to anyone who understands the neurologic and organic foundations of behavior. Psychomotor disturbances comprise a prominent part of the general behavior picture of these children. They so often are so erratic, uncoordinated, uncontrolled, and seemingly uninhibited that it is not surprising to find most other children cool and unaccepting toward them. To this rejection, a brain-injured child may respond as *catastrophically* as he often does to other frustrating situations in his life. When such children display emotions, they usually do so very intensely.*

When a child's behavior description needs such terms as the following, the possibility of brain and central nervous system injury—perhaps subtle and hard to demonstrate frankly— should be kept in mind in trying to help him:

—— quite restless, with a general hyperactivity about him
—— easily distracted by minor stimuli
—— very impulsive, seems unable to manage transient desires
—— sometimes may seem quite flighty
—— high desire to chatter, often very talkative
—— emotionally unstable
—— responses frequently are very intense
—— low self-control, may seem quite violent and cruel when angry

Child's health history

The brain and central nervous system are not intended to

*W. B. Cannon's clinical observations of children with possible brain injuries led him to believe such youngsters often find themselves driven by intense subcortical and thalamic impulses that are beyond usual control by the child himself. Out of my own experience, I have come to agree largely with Cannon about children who feel very jittery.

be exposed to severe stress or infection. The blood vessels that supply extrapyramidal areas in the brain, for example, are quite vulnerable to head pressures at birth. Intracranial hemorrhage in these areas is believed to be a major cause of the kinds of difficulties being discussed in these chapters. Brain cells and fibers are very sensitive to oxygen deprivation, as well as to many endogenous and exogenous toxins.

Good teachers do not rush in to ask questions that alarm parents who are already too sensitive and fearful about a child. Yet parents often do need to talk to a warmhearted teacher about the child. The conversation may provide answers to these questions:

——Were there hazardous pre-natal conditions?
  (Spotting; hemorrhage; severe infections; tendencies to abort?)
——Was gestation normal in length?
  (Much less, or much longer, than expected full term?)
——Was Caesarean section necessary?
  (Any complications?)
——Was labor hazardous to baby?
  (Very long; precipitate; very hard; dry birth?)
——Was mother in much danger during labor?
  (Eclampsia; pelvic malformation; antipartum hemorrhage?)
——Did baby suffer much during birth?
  (Difficult presentation; twisting of the cord; forceps injury; injury from anesthesia or drugs?)
——Did baby suffer injury in early months of life?
  (Severe illnesses such as pneumonia; scarlet fever; measles; whooping cough; RH factor damage?)
——Was there any encephalitis, meningitis, in early years?
  (What sequelae can mother recall, such as changes in child's behavior, personality, learning ability?)
——Was there any trauma to head, especially in early years?
  (Hard falls, blows, that resulted in cranial fractures or concussions. What sequelae does mother recall?)

——Have there been any inflammatory diseases, especially with high fevers, that seemed to change the child's behavior or personality in some way?
——Was the child notably late in beginning to walk?
(Children with no motor impairment are usually walking alone by 16 months of age.)
——Was the child late in beginning to talk?
(Children who are not talking—using short sentences—fairly well by 28 months may reflect neurological trouble.)
——Has the child needed extra care and help for any reason?
(Slow in developing; not a strong child; allergic, etc. Is the child still troubled by health problems?)

Of course such information should always be regarded in genuine confidence and never used in any way that may alarm a parent or hurt the child.

The child's school record

Carefully scanning the progress records may bring to light many important notes of other teachers about the child. Such records of course should be viewed with sufficient wisdom not to interpret them too factually about a particular boy or girl. Yet school records may reveal earlier facets of the child's difficulties in learning that have clinical implications for possible causes of the trouble.

School-achievement scores of children above third grade can throw considerable light on possible neurological problems, as was discussed earlier in this chapter. The following brief outline will help the teacher appraise the child now, as he is trying to learn in school:

——How extensive is the child's knowledge of words?
How ably can he express his ideas?
——In comparison with his general comprehension level, how capable does he seem now in:
.........Reading   ....Spelling
.........Arithmetic   ....Number understanding

76

—— What specific troubles does he exhibit in these areas?
.........Aphasic troubles ....Recall difficulties
.........Attention difficulty ....Other
—— How well is he doing in Art?
What peculiarities does he show?
—— How well is he doing in Music and Rhythm?
What peculiarities does he show?
—— What about his motor-coordination?
Large-muscle control peculiarities?
Fine-muscle coordination anomalies?
—— Does he have difficulty in visualizing?
Is this worse at times?
—— How discouraged does he seem about school now?
(Anxiety and discouragement can add greatly to the child's learning problems, until he feels totally unable to do anything worthwhile, thus manifolding the original trouble overwhelmingly for the child.)

Does the child show any speech peculiarities?

Speech difficulties could have neurological implications in some cases. Complete examination should be made only by a well qualified person such as the speech clinician, but the teacher should be aware of some techniques for screening such children for referral.

Naming is a very vulnerable function of speech. Any disturbances of this ability in a child should alert the teacher to possible neurological implications. Children who sustained brain injuries, particularly in the dominant hemisphere, may show such disturbances along with other aphasic symptoms.

—— Ask the child to name various commonplace articles such as a knife, a jack, an eraser, a finger ring, a shoehorn, a ballpoint pen, a quarter, a key, a pocket comb, a shoelace. The test is most effective when the child is asked just to name the object when the teacher points to it, without any conversation involving the object. No cues should be offered the child.

Note the availability of the correct noun for the object, and any tendency to use circumlocutions instead of the name itself. For example: (knife) "something to cut"; (key) "for a door."

Note any tendency toward perseveration: giving the same name to several objects in the series.

——Ask the child to read aloud several new paragraphs in a book he probably can manage silently. Notice any tendency to misread words (paralexia). Surprising as it might seem, such disturbances do not necessarily pull down the child's general reading comprehension.

——Ask the child to spell and write a list of everyday words that he can use. In most aphasia cases, there are marked defects in writing and spelling. Perseveration often is more noticeable in those areas than in speech.

——Ask the child to repeat such phrases as: "Six kittens in a basket"; "the car sped swiftly down the road"; "two elephants at the circus." Notice any slurring, or jamming of letter sounds. (Children over eight who reflect no neurological impairment can repeat such mixed diphthongs as occur in *Methodist Episcopal* fairly well.)

Are there disturbances in the use of numbers?

Such disturbances can occur following lesions of various areas of the cortex. Arithmetic processes are very vulnerable to brain injury. Subtraction and division usually are more disturbed than addition and multiplication. Some children seem unable to remember the original problem, and to apply the proper operation to achieve the answer desired. These difficulties, especially in a youngster who otherwise seems to be bright enough, may reflect cortical dysfunctions.

——Ask the child to write down digits and numbers from dictation. Give him simple additions, subtractions, multiplications, and divisions to perform on paper, progressing to more difficult calculations according to how well the child succeeds.

78

——Younger children respond with interest when asked to count out blocks, or make a certain number of dots on the paper. They like to tell which is bigger, 6 or 9, 10 or 7. Care must be used, of course, to keep these tests within the child's estimated intellectual level. If the child is feeling very jittery or anxious, he should not be given these tests until he feels calmer.

Does the child have difficulty in copying?

The copying of jittery children is usually less disturbed than their writing. If the child has much difficulty in copying simple designs, for example, there probably are complicating perceptual factors of a constructional apraxia nature. In any case, such a child needs special school help in many learning tasks.

——Have the child do his best in copying a series of simple geometric forms, such as a square, diamond, triangle, and a circle-square overlapping. The models should be neatly drawn in broad black lines (with a wide point felt pen) on white cards. Designs should be about one and one-half to two inches in size. Ask the child to copy one design at a time, in pencil, on his letter-size white paper.

Notice particularly how the child goes about this task— how sure he seems about himself; how he perceives any mistakes he makes.

Does the child have difficulty in reproducing designs from memory?

Ability to reproduce what was seen for just a few seconds is a very sensitive brain function easily disturbed by even subtle injuries.

Ask the child to do his best in drawing simple designs he has been shown for about five seconds, in good light. The designs to be presented should be drawn in broad black lines on white cards. Each figure should be large enough to prevent vision problems from harming the test procedure. Five-second exposure usually is sufficient. Such designs as these may be used with most children over eight

Some designs that may be used with children over 8:
Put each design on a separate card.

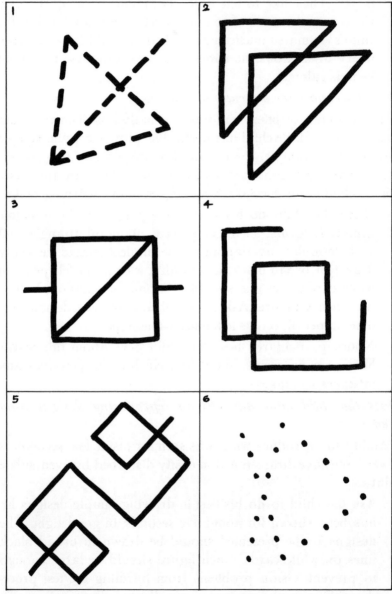

68% actual size

Simpler designs should be used with younger children.

68% actual size

This is how Gary, 14, and doing fairly well in an excellent special class in junior high, duplicated the previous designs from memory, after ten-second exposures. Medical records noted precipitate birth; possible cerebral injury. Two EEGs, when Gary was nearly 11 and later at 13, showed signs of brain injury. The boy has often been jittery in school, with many irritable spells. He tried very hard to draw the designs well.

years old; simpler ones are necessary with younger children.

Note especially any additions, omissions, or peculiar changes the child makes in reproducing each design. These often reflect the kind of difficulty the child has been finding in schoolwork too. Perceptual trouble will be apparent to an alert teacher. Of course the child's figures should be viewed in light of normal development. A child who tends very much to *rotate* such figures from the original may be reflecting subtle cerebral dysfunction or injury.

Does the child have difficulty in separating a figure from the background?

Many boys and girls who have trouble in managing figure-background relationships also have considerable difficulty in most academic areas in school, especially reading, spelling, and arithmetic. Abstractive ability is quite vulnerable to brain injury or disturbance.

— Ask the child to do his best in reproducing from memory (after five-second exposure) simple drawings of common objects that are drawn in broad black lines on an overall background motif. The two suggestions below will give the teacher the idea:

Other figure-background combinations might include a

70% actual size

82

bucket with zig-zag lightning background; a truck, with trees; a house, with chains of circles.

Notice how hard the child must work to keep from involving the highly patterned background in his own drawing.

——Similar cards may be used to discover how well the child can resist the background motif as he copies the main figure directly.

Notice any disturbances caused by these tasks in the child's methods of meeting the problems, as well as in his procedures. Especially in children over ten, difficulty in establishing and maintaining adequate figure-background relationships may reflect subtle neurological disturbances or dysfunctions.

Does the child show disturbances in his right-left orientation?

Some pathologic cerebral conditions disturb the child's normal sense of his body and its positional relationships. Even when these disturbances are slight, they are still involved in such complicated processes as reading and arithmetic where the right-left directionality of performance is important. There are many simple ways to test this:

——Ask the child to turn right or left, or all the way around. Have him touch his left ear with the right hand, and so on. Notice any directional hesitancies or errors; check these with more requests.

——Have the child tell whether various objects in the room are on his right or left. Notice any increased confusion as the child answers more questions, or as the questions become more complicated.

Can the child clearly differentiate his fingers?

Finger agnosia often reflects brain dysfunction, and is always suspect in a child who is having much trouble in behavior and learning. Right-left disorientation usually accompanies finger agnosia. The full syndrome (Gerstmann's syndrome) usually is found in cases of general spatial disturbance, nominal aphasia and acalculia. The parieto-occipital regions of the brain probably have suffered some lesion in these cases, usually in the dominant hemisphere. Children generally like to do these things:

——Have the child place his hand flat on the paper, so the teacher can draw around it with a pencil. Number the nails 1 to 5, on the hand outline.

Hold the child's hand beneath the table, out of his sight. Touch one of the fingers for a second or two; ask him to tell what finger (number) on the outline would be the same as was touched. Several variations of this procedure are equally reliable.

Notice all errors and hesitations, particularly in children over eight.

Can the child identify the body midline?

Children who feel very anxious sometimes have a little trouble in doing this, tending to respond to the test before the body midline has been reached, as though in rather intense anticipation. This should not be surprising in an apprehensive youngster. Children who may have sustained cerebral injury sometimes are unable to sense body midline and may respond quite a distance beyond the center. The method of checking a child is simple enough to do, but the particular child's responses should be interpreted guardedly.

——Have the child keep eyes closed while you trace with your finger the midline of his forehead, up and down perhaps twice. Tell him this is the midline of his forehead. While the child's eyes are still closed, tell him you are drawing a line with your finger across his forehead now, and he is to tell when your finger is at the midline. Try this from left to right and right to left, tracing the midline before each trial. Note the child's errors of identification, but of course, do not let him feel any sense of failure.

Can the child recognize letters traced on his palms or cheeks?

Many children with subtle tactile disturbances (and body image distortions) have marked difficulty in doing this.

—— Ask the child to keep his eyes closed and tell you what letter (or simple form) you are tracing on his cheek or palm. Trace such letters and forms as C, E, M,□, + , or △ , that the child is likely to know by sight. Note the kinds of errors he makes. Children with reading difficulty rising out of deeper imperception often have trouble in responding to this test of graphesthesia.

Does the child need to develop better laterality?

Children who have not yet developed unilaterality of dominance comprise the largest group with reading, spelling, and arithmetic difficulties. Well developed laterality and smooth motor coordination are paramount in reading readiness. Hand, foot, eye, and ear dominance should be all right-sided or left-sided, for best learning conditions in the brain. Mixed dominance may reflect simply an immaturity of these organizations in younger children, or the organic dysfunction or disturbance of a central nervous subsystem.

—— Watch the child at play and work; notice his hand and foot preferences: using a pencil, cutting paper, reaching for a cup, holding a spoon, catching a ball, spinning a jack, stepping down from a chair, kicking a can, patting down sand, and drawing a picture with a crayon held by the toes.

—— Notice the ear he prefers to use to listen to a watch.

With his eyes closed, notice how accurately the child can point with his nose to a clock or little bell a few feet ahead of him in a quiet room. Ear dominance is not easy to test with some children who feel tense or jittery, but it still should be kept in mind in the total clinical picture of any child who is having school difficulty.

—— Eye dominance is easier to test, with most children. Ask the child to imagine that a cardboard tube is a pirate's telescope, and he is the pirate looking for a treasure island. Note how many times out of several trials the child uses the right or left eye.

85

Check with this test: Cut a 1-inch hole in the center of an 8 x 10 piece of paper. Have the child hold the paper out at arms' length with both hands, facing the teacher. Hold a pencil (or some bright object) just behind the paper, so the eraser is visible to the child through the hole. Ask him to move the paper gradually toward his eyes, but to keep the eraser plainly in sight all the time. Repeat the test several times, to be sure of eye dominance. (This test often surprises both child and teacher.)

Does the child seem hypersensitive to bright flashing lights?

Many children with suspected or known cerebral injury can be *triggered* by rapidly moving or flashing lights. The critical flicker frequency for one child may not bother another youngster nearly as much. As with all such signs in children, this one must always be regarded simply as possibly indicating hypersensitivity. About five per cent of children felt to be normal enough otherwise in school react to certain flicker frequencies quite like children with clinical signs of epilepsy. Some children say they feel strangely faint and woozy when they have to look at flickering or rapidly moving lights. This is not simply a neurotic behavior, but probably points to cerebral difficulty of the kind so often found in jittery boys and girls.

——The child can ordinarily recall having such trouble or not. Calmly taking with him about the matter would be sufficient to alert the teacher, rather than employing any test method that might make the child feel upset.

Does the child show vision signals of possible organicity?

No teacher who is wise about life *and* children ever overlooks the possibility of vision problems in the youngster who has trouble with reading and spelling, drawing and copying, catching a ball, or any other seeing activity. Every thoughtful teacher is in a unique position to notice children who may have such trouble. Snellen charts are not the only technique for guessing that a child may have a vision problem.

No screening test has been as serviceable in spotting these boys and girls in the classroom as an observant teacher and her records of each child's performance. Combined with good vision screening tests, usually given by the school nurse, the teacher's observations of the children in a class can locate those with vision difficulties.

The American Optical Association's committee on vision problems of school children has compiled a checklist of signals that teachers ought to notice. The committee strongly recommends that all children be sent for *complete* visual examination who:

—— are poor achievers, particularly if their potentials seem much better than their achievement.

—— may not be failing, yet who do not seem to be working up to reasonably expectable levels or capacity.

These broad screening pointers will help to discern many of the children who deserve careful professional visual analysis to discover any physical difficulties. Beyond these broad guides, there are further cues in children's behavior that should alert teachers to suspect vision troubles that need professional help:

—— Does the child seem to dislike reading?
—— Does he often lose his place while reading?
—— Does he seem to avoid close work?
—— Is his sitting posture peculiar or poor when he is reading?
—— Does he often skip lines or reread words?
—— Does he have many reversals when he reads?
—— Does he hold the page very close to his eyes?
—— Does he often squint, frown, or blink when he reads?
—— Does his head move excessively when he reads?
—— Do similar letters (a, o; m, n; etc.) confuse him?
—— Does close work seem to make him tense?
—— Does he often rub his eyes?

These signals sometimes reflect inadequate vision in a child, but other causes may bring many of these signals too. Only a complete study of the child by the specialist skilled in such examinations will determine if the youngster has a significant vision problem. In any case, checking all children who *may* have such difficulties is well worth the effort.

Does the child show signals of hearing trouble?

Children who have severe hearing loss generally are easier for the teacher to spot than girls or boys who have a moderate loss. Such children often are labeled as "inattentive" or "preoccupied," while the real trouble remains unsuspected for a long time. Younger children do not always realize they may not be hearing accurately. But there are signals that a good teacher can catch in the classroom, and check by closer conversation with the youngster. It is wise teaching practice to check further for possible hearing difficulty any child who:

— behaves in peculiar ways when other children or grownups talk around him or to him.
— does not seem to pay normal attention to music or other sounds, especially at low volume.
— is getting along poorly in schoolwork, especially in *language* areas.
— has complained of earaches.
— seems to favor one ear, by turning this ear even slightly toward the source of a sound.
— has complained of "head noises" or that an ear has seemed "closed up."
— frequently holds or rubs an ear.
— has trouble in pronouncing words or spelling them.
— has a history of ear infection.

Any of these signals in a child should keep the teacher alert to possible hearing trouble as a cause of the school problem. Good schools now are prompt in having the school nurse and physician examine such children and send them to the otologist when necessary for complete hearing tests. Such precautions are saving many boys and girls from serious emotional and learning complications.

88

One fact about these problems has been self-evident to me in all the schools where I have worked: School physicians, school nurses, speech clinicians, counselors, psychologists, reading teachers, and other specialists are open to thoughtful help from any teacher who is interested in children. Parents can be valuable members of such a multidiscipline team too. So can the children themselves. In all good schools, children can be referred for help by their parents, and by themselves.

6

EMOTIONAL CONFLICTS OFTEN CLOUD THE PICTURE . . .

Children suffer from discouragement and depression more than has been commonly believed. Many children feel lost and have no hope for themselves. This can be especially so for girls and boys who are failing even though they try hard to do the work.

However guarded from open view by antics and defenses, feelings of despair and depression soon make whatever other school and behavior problems had existed, much worse to try to fathom. It is not surprising that such a child can go quite misunderstood for long periods.

Children, unlike adults, usually are able to be active and appear *completely absorbed in interesting situations* around them even while depressed and anxious. This difference may lead grownups to overlook the signals of depression and anxiety in a child. "Come on there," the grownup may say to the child, "at your age what can be so bad to make you feel upset? . . . Don't be afraid anymore, everything will work out all right . . . ."

But life is not so easy or simple as that, for children who must somehow meet difficulties that are insurmountable in many ways. No child who can come to school could be slow enough not to know when he fails to meet important standards. Giving him *passing* marks on report cards, and moving him along to the next grade *anyway* never really fools him. Secretly, he knows—much more than he sometimes lets us see—what troubles he will have to face.

The potential dangers of chronic emotional stress have often been underrated, particularly among people who like to believe that anyone can be rugged and invincible by saying so hard enough. The emergence of cardiovascular disturbance and disease as one of the chief causes of disability and death has led to intensive search for underlying processes. More and more studies are showing that essential (idiopathic) hypertension can exist without any evidence of obviously related disease processes.

Blood pressure does rise when we are very angry or fearful. This is understandable enough to any biologist who is aware of the triggering mechanisms in the glandular and neural networks. A big question has remained, however: How do supposedly *mild and ordinary* feelings of conflict set the same biochemical processes going at times in some of us? Are our emotional threshholds quite variable? What part might a child's previous feelings have in the triggering equation?

The search for answers to these questions has had some success in recent years. We are now much more aware of psychic factors beneath many of the respiratory disorders, allergies, skin sensitivities, headaches, glandular upsets, and gastric difficulties that plague our children as well as ourselves. The cause and effect relationship between even mild but chronic emotions and organic functions is a circular *interaction,* as Paul Schilder was insisting thirty years ago.

A discouraged child can suffer loss of appetite, or seem unable to get enough food. Vomiting often is psychogenic. Twenty years ago, H. G. Wolff was showing that emotional conflicts involving anxiety, hostility, and resentment produce *profound* gastric changes that can lead to ulceration. Several studies in recent years have found high incidences of gastric ulcer in children who are having school trouble.

Every child under such stresses may not show drastic physical changes. Children still vary widely in temperament, and some are able to withstand more emotional loading than others.

√ Children who for any reason feel unvalued and rejected are more apt to show signs of discouragement when things go wrong in school. The major cause of neurotic depression in children of all ages is the feeling of not being loved.

Boys and girls still in their latency years (pre-adolescents) may be considerably depressed and upset emotionally without being fully aware of it. Schoolwork may suffer with language and reading skills showing the worst troubles. If there happens to be subtle perceptual-motor involvement too, the combination may present symptoms that are very hard to differentiate from psychosis.

√ When a child feels loved and valued, he is more likely to be relaxed and open to the right help. This is simply part of the wider cholinergic changes that accompany such a feeling as a warmly valued person. Children are swift to sense the teacher's *genuine* affection and respond to it in terms of increased readiness to learn.

Feelings, quite as emotions, can arouse impulses to act, as well as physiological changes. The two go hand-in-hand.

It is not surprising that fear reduces a child's learning effectiveness, or that the connecting link is organic. Fear excites the sympathetic nervous system and induces adrenalin secretion into the blood. This in turn has many undesirable effects on the body when continued very long. We can stand short episodes of intense fear, but results are always bad when the situation goes· on for a long time. This is so obvious in fearful children.

Both fear and anger are spurs to action. All of us are aware of this psychobiological fact in our own daily lives. Yet, when the action does not remove us from the danger, we begin to bog down in despair and even neurotic inaction and lethargy. Especially in children, the economy of all the organ systems is swiftly impaired.

The surface signals of subtle, chronic discouragement vary a little, child to child, as they do in older persons. One child may gradually withdraw, while another may be ready to battle at the slightest touch. Still another may show peculiar learning *blocks* that may go misdiagnosed for a long while. Every teacher has seen such youngsters.

Children can feel ashamed (and discouraged) even when nobody else finds out. Shame and embarrassment are never simple emotions, but always involve sadness and dejection combined with fear of loss of love and self-esteem. Children who are in danger of failing, for example, usually have widening fears of many other *consequences* of their inability. Such a feeling frequently generates neurotic guilt in the unhappy boy or girl.

Just as chronic, secret fear may gradually result in disabling anxiety, so may a child's feelings of remorse and resentment develop into guilt that is diffuse and free floating. Such guilt can seep into all activities without recognizable connections with the roots from which it came. These feelings are exceedingly hard to probe in many children.

Eleven-year-old Erica's teacher referred the girl to the psychologist at the guidance center because she seemed so tense and jittery. The child was above average in intellectual capacity. Her WISC performance rated her at least 130 IQ. Yet she could not concentrate on her schoolwork and was heading for failing marks.

At first Erica insisted that she was not upset or anxious about anything. "Why should I be worried about school—or anything? . . . I don't see why the teacher says I am so restless or tense . . . . Maybe I worry a little sometimes, but nobody knows it but me, I haven't told anybody else. . . ."

The school physician knew that Erica's father had been somewhat depressive at times, and her mother was inclined to worry. The parents were not sure whether the girl knew about their problems. They had presumed she knew little at most. Actually Erica had known for quite some time, and secretly felt that she was the cause, especially of her father's condition.

At eleven, she was unable to accept some of the deeper reasons why her parents' mild emotional illness troubled her so greatly. The school physician and psychologist decided not to probe too much, since the mother herself seemed reluctant to let anyone help the girl by psychotherapy. Erica did regain happier feelings about herself in a few weeks, partly through the warm understanding the teacher was able to establish with the girl. Her schoolwork improved remarkably by the end of the semester.

When she was sixteen and in tenth grade, Erica's counselor noticed that the girl frequently seemed very lonely and depressed again. Any mention of her mother or father made tears appear in her eyes. The father was still under special medical care for a heart condition. "If he died, it would be my fault. I have been such a worry to him," she confided.

This time the psychologist was able to persuade Erica to talk about the deeper anxieties that had been dogging her heels so long. Her depressive feelings gradually diminished as she came to recognize their veiled sources and meanings. A conference with the family physician was helpful in reassuring Erica that her father needed special care but was not in great danger.

In her senior year in high school, the girl still was having a little trouble with math and science. The psychologist felt this difficulty had always been based largely in perceptual-motor disability that had been more evident earlier. The emotional overlay in her life had often made her teachers blame all the child's difficulties on this factor.

When a child is not behaving very badly, teachers sometimes conclude that the youngster has no disabling anxieties about himself. Many teachers rarely attempt to encourage a child to reveal *how he feels about himself.* Fortunately this picture is changing in some places, as alert teachers are coming to see how much a child's *self-image* can affect his whole life, at home as well as on the playground and in the classroom.

94

Discouraged children can be helped very much by teachers who take time to listen attentively and avoid authoritative attitudes. Anxiety does not respond to *logic*, however sincerely it is offered. Yet some facts about real life do help these boys and girls, even when the facts are unpleasant. Left without such *reality limits*, discouraged children sometimes drift in moody spells with many bizarre and fantastic ideas about themselves and the world around them.

Reality can be very rewardingly therapeutic for children who must come to grips intelligently with certain difficulties they face. This is true for boys and girls who have perceptual-motor dysfunctions that may have to be faced and managed a long time. Here is where the teacher can do a marvelous job in showing such a child that he is not mentally deficient just because he happens to have trouble in reading, math, or science. Reality therapy enables such a girl or boy to perceive what he *has* and how it can be used to build a useful and successful life.

Every warmhearted teacher with much experience can remember many discouraged, jittery youngsters who were turned away from early delinquent trends by the right concern *plus wise, steady control* for a while. *Early* recognition affords good treatment *early* enough to be most effective. Many alert schools now employ special tutors who are skilled in helping children regain courage and a sense of being valued. One reading and math tutor I knew a few years ago in a school system was expert at the job of enabling children with signs of minimal brain damage to take new hope about themselves. The changes in her young charges at times were junior miracles. Most of the *emotional blocks* disappeared in the children she tutored, even though their actual school skills did not greatly improve.

Children who feel very upset emotionally much of the time still can benefit from the right kind of school situation. These children especially need a school climate that is conducive to personal hope and courage. Teaching these boys and girls requires an orientation and goals that differ markedly from the usual point of view and aims of teachers in programs for normal children. For comparison, some of the commonly accepted—and educationally understandable—goals for normal children are listed here:

——Help each child attain mastery of a specialized body of useful knowledge, to the best of his ability.

——Spur each child to be as creative as possible in utilizing his talents and capacities.

——Urge each child to expand his horizons as widely as possible, in keeping with excellent social and ethical standards.

——Press each girl and boy to discover high challenge in every learning experience.

These goals are surely in line with the rightful expectations of good parents for their children. In large measure, these same long range goals are part of the undergirding philosophy of education for other children who are less able to learn.

Wise teachers (and parents), however, have come to realize that children who are discouraged about themselves need school programs based on more immediate and essential goals. Children with perceptual-motor and/or emotional difficulties especially need classroom programs that aim first of all to:

——Nurture sturdy feelings of self-confidence and courage, along with a warm sense of being valued as a real person.

——Diminish the old neurotic fears and anxieties.

These goals are more difficult to attain than the acquisition of knowledge, skill, and creativeness. The teacher must have keener insight into the *dynamics* of confidence and courage, as well as fear and anxiety. The teacher must know how to invent and employ classroom methods not usually needed with more normal children who are getting along fairly well.

The *special teacher* must be wisely capable in helping each child:

——Begin to build interpersonal relationships that are freer and less distorting than before. (The teacher's own genuine feeling and behavior toward the child is the catalyst here.)

——Begin to manage anxiety and fear a little better. (Here, the teacher's skill in keeping expectations of the child within limits the child can meet is paramount.)

——Begin to face reality with more resiliency. (The teacher's ability to present benign—yet interesting—life situations can help the child learn how to face them better.)

——Begin to find exhilaration and satisfaction in learning. (The teacher can nourish the child's efforts by emphasizing nonpainful, nonalarming, pleasurable, ego-supporting facets of learning.)

These goals quickly test the teacher's own emotional stability, insight, and empathy. *Understanding* any child demands far more than correcting his spelling errors. Wholehearted acceptance of an upset child, while still keeping him in the right control, has never been easily accomplished. Whatever it takes, a large part of the prescription probably is the kind of wisdom that comes out of healthy personal experience with life values.

No one person has the corner on such experience and wisdom. Yet a team of openminded, intelligent, skilled people can generate enough of it to do the job remarkably well with children who have felt discouraged and hopeless about themselves.

Bring together in a warmly cooperating team a substantial teacher, counselor, clinician, school psychologist, school physician, and nurse, and their combined brainpower is far greater than the sum of their separate capacities to help disturbed youngsters. This comes as no surprise to any teacher who has been working on such a team.

All these programs and services cost more money and demand greater investments of genuinely dedicated hearts and well-trained minds. Yet none of these efforts can be summed up simply in dollars and services. The rebuilding of any child who has felt terribly discouraged and lost, so that he takes new courage to go ahead again, is immeasurable. Every child, however apparently disabled by what happened to him, still has such possibilities.

Experienced teachers in good special education programs know how much the right combination of *calm, steady discipline* plus *good life-space structure* can help children who are emotionally disturbed, from whatever cause. In these circumstances, such children grow and gain sometimes in so many ways that it seems miraculous. And perhaps it is; I have often thought so, as I saw teachers and teams somehow setting the situation for such things to happen to the children in their care.

In fact, special classes and even special schools need not be the permanent places for the majority of children who have suffered schizophrenic breaks, cerebral damage, or neurotic deviations. Much of their recovery possibilities depends on the teacher's capacity to *implement* the knowledge and insight we now have into the dynamics of children's physical, intellectual, and emotional development. This has been the front edge of the great changes I have seen so many teachers accomplishing with children who used to be discouraged and weary of trying.

Within such programs and classrooms, many children who have been very disturbed come to believe in themselves and in their personal worth and value. They grow in ability to manage their impulses in better and more acceptable ways. They learn to make new, wholesome, and warmly meaningful personal relationships, valuing these above relationships with inanimate things.

They learn how to invest emotional energies toward new and happier goals, in school, at home, and out in the wider world. Better habits and behavior gradually replace poorer ones. Healthier attitudes begin to emerge. And on these foundations, knowledge and skills can develop toward life fulfillment.

These goals are possible wherever thoughtful teachers determine to make them a reality.

In past years some teachers have felt that their job did not really include trying to help children who were quite disturbed and unable to learn as well as other girls and boys. The range of excuses such teachers offer is sometimes jolting to realize:

"Emotionally upset children disturb me even more, so how can you expect me to teach such youngsters?"

"My experience has not been with such children, I would not know how to manage them well enough."

"That job probably would discourage me after awhile."

Fortunately there always are other teachers around who find real challenges in helping children who have complex problems.

These teachers personify the true meaning of the word *educator:* To draw out the child so that all his powers—intellectual, physical, and moral—develop harmoniously toward fullest stature for this particular child. A good teacher does far more than impart knowledge and promote subject learning.

The task of helping discouraged children just won't wait until all the expertly trained people are available. This is why practical-minded communities are tackling the job with the people who *are* available.

Psychiatrists and clinical psychologists having extensive experience with emotionally disturbed children have never been in high supply. Experienced social workers are not plentiful in many areas, nor are well-trained counselors. There may never be enough such persons to cover all the school communities that might call for help with children who seem headed for trouble.

This fact of life has been alerting many schools to come up with practical answers to the problems of recognizing such children early enough, and providing some programs that can help. Communities within a hundred miles of universities with departments of psychiatry, psychology, and social work (in addition to education and guidance) are utilizing consultative help from these reservoirs. Special education departments usually are willing to help as consultants to schools desiring this.

Experienced special class teachers and school psychologists, in team-work with school physicians, can boost the insight and skill of good *regular* teachers even in a few inservice meetings to discuss children with learning difficulties. As the psychologist in a county school system, I saw such inservice colloquia soon give really interested teachers new and effective techniques with their children.

The *team approach* to children in difficulty offers many advantages over any other method. When the child's teachers, parents, school psychologist, physician, nurse, and counselor *combine* their unique brainpower and knowledge in the job of figuring out how best to help the youngster, good moves are bound to happen. Schools in rural areas and small towns can do this practically as well as schools in cities that seem to have more advantages.

Such team efforts always pay high dividends for any community, and any school. *All* the children of all the families benefit in ways that would have escaped imagination many times. One discouraged child who is helped to regain hope and a new concept of his potentialities makes the whole program truly successful.

7

MANY OF THESE
CHILDREN HAVE
GONE MISUNDERSTOOD
SO LONG . . .

All the children who have discouraging perceptual-motor difficulties are not boys. Girls help to increase the list too.

Laurie was nearly ten, and in most ways quite like the usual happy-but-noisy fourth-graders in her school. In other ways she was not as much like them, at least not like the ones who were doing fairly well academically. Physically she was as attractive a child as any of the rest, and she was hardly mentally slow, no matter what her usual school achievement might seem to show.

On the verbal subtests of the Wechsler Intelligence Scale for Children, Laurie rated above average for her age in such aspects as word understanding, comprehension of ideas, ability to gather and use information sensibly, and ability to catch abstract concepts. Asked to read from a carefully standardized scale, she did fairly well up to the beginning of the grade 3 level. Above this level, her reading was choppy, and she stumbled over many of the usual words at grade 4 level. Even so, Laurie could read better than many of the boys in her class.

Her arithmetic progress had not come along as well as her reading. From first grade, number concepts had given her trouble though the teachers had used excellent methods of instruction. Her handwriting had always been a problem too.

Overall, however, Laurie seemed to be bright and was getting by sufficiently by late spring not to be in danger of failing. Her work had improved very much during the year, so it seemed better to promote her and hope that she would catch up in fifth grade. At the moment, this decision resolved the school's dilemma with Laurie's parents who wanted the child promoted.

Back in second grade, she rated 87 IQ on the Stanford-Binet scale. By the end of third grade, she rated 106 on the WISC, with her responses to the verbal subtests averaging 114— enough above the mean (100) for the teacher to feel sure Laurie was not lacking in potential brainpower.

Laurie guessed we were writing about her in this chapter, and she gladly did the handwriting sample shown here. It reflects many signs of her perceptual-language-motor difficulties that had never before been considered by the school. In this sample, she copied directly from the teacher's neatly written script: *There are many other children with nearly undiscernable signs.* Laurie needed over four minutes to write this sentence:

When she was asked to write the first two lines of "Mary had a little lamb" without the teacher doing it first, Laurie accepted the task cheerfully but found it very hard:

Mary had a laillr lnnrf
itrs flerce was hurite ors smorur

She was able to read the printed lines of the couplet fairly well and told us how much she used to enjoy her mother reading the poem to her when she was a little girl. "Lambs are so cuddly, we had three on our farm last year and I liked to play with them."

Laurie was like many children who show *subclinical* signs of perceptual and expressive difficulties. Laurie's teacher said, "The signals were there. Perhaps occasionally, I saw them slightly and wondered whether to refer the girl for testing." She added that Laurie did not seem slow mentally, and had never been a behavior problem, but just did not do quite as well as might be expected in some things.

The mother came willingly to a special conference about the child, and brought some valuable insight. Laurie had not really talked until she was nearly three. The family had thought the lag was simply because three older sisters gave her so much care and attention there was little need for the child to talk. By three, this reason had begun to fade in value. But Laurie seemed to be a happy little girl otherwise, so the family did not worry much about the slow speech gain. By four, her speech appeared to be normal enough to the family, and earlier fears were forgotten. The mother brought photographs of the child around age four and five, that showed an attractive youngster who was enjoying warm rapport in a busy family. It was easy to understand how the family had overlooked some subtle signs of lagging development.

When at seven she still seemed "barely ready for school" and could not draw a man that looked better than 5-year-olds usually produce, her mother was not alarmed. "Nobody in our family has ever been much of an artist, why should the school expect Laurie to show such talent at her age?" The same reasoning kept the parents calm when Laurie found great difficulty in catching on to reading and number concepts. "We're just not brains in our family. She is bright enough, and some day she will begin to do as well as other children in school."

All this was marvelously wiser than nagging and scolding the child to do better. When she was first referred for psychological evaluation in grade 4, Laurie felt very secure and valued at home, with no great worries about school. "Even when I don't do as well as my brother, my mother and father love me anyway."

The only puzzle in the school picture was whether the teachers had not kept accurate notes on Laurie's progress, or had not perceived any signals of the child's real difficulty. The first-grade teacher had noted that the child was "much more capable than her work has shown, but this will clear up in the next year I am confident."

The second-grade teacher wrote, "Laurie will learn to read all right, she just isn't ready to settle down to arithmetic yet. Stricter home control might help, or perhaps a tutor. Try some of the new flash cards now in many stores." Here was an attractive child going through two years in school with no one taking time to notice signs of trouble just a little way ahead. She was nearly ten and in fourth grade before she was called to the attention of the psychologist when a new principal was taking a closer look at the children in each grade.

Laurie's responses to some of the WISC subtests threw clearer light on possible sources of her difficulties. On the digit-span subtest, for example, a child is asked to listen carefully as the clinician says several digits slowly, and then repeat the numbers exactly as they were given. In the second part of this subtest, the child is instructed to *reverse* the numbers when repeating them. A very poor score on this subtest, compared with other subtest scores, is seen in many children with known cerebral dysfunction. A poor digit-span score still would not, in itself, justify firm preclusion in a particular case. It would simply be one indication that the child has great difficulty in sequencing some kinds of abstract things. Experienced psychologists bear such precautions in mind in examining any child. Laurie did poorly on this subtest.

Performance on the object-assembly subtest threw further light on her perception difficulties. In this test the child must assemble the pieces of a simple manikin figure, a horse, a face, and a car. Ten-year-olds who are having no school-

*Laurie first placed this piece with the legs *up in the air,* and finally moved it to the position shown here.

learning problems have no trouble in assembling these relatively simple objects.

The *manikin* assembly was not too hard for her, though at first she did not seem to notice that the feet needed to be reversed to fit best. The *face* puzzle gave her great trouble, and the *car* was even harder to assemble. Sometimes she seemed unable to see when the pieces were correctly placed, and she moved them into other relationships that were incorrect. When she had done her best to assemble the *horse* she said, "Well, there's something wrong with him, but this is the best I can do." The assembly took her nearly four minutes.

She had grown up on a farm, with several fine horses around her all her life. She could ride one of them very well—yet she found this test very difficult. The deeper reason was not anxiety or a slow brain, but visual imperception that had gone largely undiagnosed even by the good teachers who had been trying to help her.

This was understandable enough. The child usually was calm and happy enough, not jittery and rambunctious and *into everything* as many youngsters are who show more severe perceptual-motor signs. Her mother said the child had rarely been very upset or hard to manage. She could stand quietly, heels together and eyes closed. She could hold her hands very still, out in front of her, with her eyes closed. She walked very well on tiptoes, and also on her heels. She could repeat a complex little story quite well when she was asked to do it.

But on the block-design subtest of the WISC, she did very poorly. Secretly anxious children sometimes do poorly on this test, but anxiety could be ruled out in Laurie's case. A more likely possibility was the kind of perceptual difficulty she reflected in assembling the horse.

Exactly what organic dysfunction, lesion, or other factor was causing Laurie to do so poorly on such tests—and in writing, reading, spelling, and arithmetic—would have been very hard to state with certainty. There are increasing data from many studies to support the hypothesis that many children are born with a real predisposition toward the kind of perceptual confusion of symbols that Laurie showed. Some hereditary factor may be involved in many of these children. As yet, the percentage cannot be stated. In Laurie's case, her test responses did seem to reflect the *kinds of trouble* she had been finding in several school subjects. This enabled the school to take the right strides to help her in ways that turned out to be quite effective. Kephart's general techniques already were in common use in Laurie's school.

Now at fifteen, she is in ninth grade, an attractive girl who feels confident about herself. She has become a self-actualizing young person, with practical warm hope about the future. She is looking forward with a healthy mixture of anticipation and expectation to completing high school and then finding a job in a nursery school. "I like little children and I think they will like to have me help them."

Math and spelling troubles still tag her a little but she manages to keep her marks up in the low C range with extra study whenever necessary. Her parents deserve much of the credit for showing her how to go ahead with courage and hard work directed in the right ways.

She has learned to type moderately well, with few glaring errors. Her handwriting still is not as good as she wishes it were. Typing has partly circumvented this old problem. A thoughtful counselor in fifth grade suggested that she try to learn to type, even if she turned out to be a slow typist. The suggestion was a good one. Though she has never won a speed test, she can type quite well now, and this extra skill has been an asset to her.

Some of her earlier school troubles were reflected in a new light last year, when she had an electroencephalogram to check on her jittery feelings. The EEG showed *mild, diffuse dysrhythmia of non-specific type, with slight focal discharges in the occipital area.* This was hardly surprising in view of the old perceptual-motor difficulties that had dogged her school progress so long. The great advances in psychological testing in the last few years have done more than anything else to identify children like Laurie early in their lives, when they can best be helped.

Tom is another interesting case in point. At fifteen and in grade 7, he likes to pour over popular magazines about racing cars and new engines. He will be promoted to grade 8 because he seems to be working as hard as he can in school. On such reading scales as the Gilmore or the Durrell, he scores about grade 5 level, two grades below his class placement. A thorough neurological examination a year ago revealed no clear symptoms of a cerebral lesion that might account for the boy's continuing reading difficulties. He has consistently rated above average on individual intelligence tests such as the WISC, with the only signs of possible dysfunction in perception.

The remedial teacher who has been working with Tom this

87% actual size

year gave the boy a special test involving ability to reproduce simple designs from memory following ten-second exposures. Here are three of Tom's drawings on this test that reveal something of the underlying difficulty the boy faces most of the time.

Notice the kind of imperceptions Tom's reproductions reflect, and his reading difficulties become more understandable. That the boy has learned to read anywhere near his present grade 5 level is a small miracle in many ways.

He is a handsome lad, with pleasant and likable manners, and this probably has encouraged his teachers to try to help him and to boost the marks on his report cards a little sometimes. But Tom will face increasing troubles in upper grades when he tackles many of the courses he hopes to take in the new vocational high school. Whatever the deeper neurological problem may be, his brain cells and nerves simply do not give him the same percepts that my nervous system gives me when I look at diagrams and figures. If my perceptions are correct and accurate, his surely are neither. The drawings and diagrams that make sense to me must give Tom a real sense of frustration and discouragement.

Yet he is a bright boy in a thousand ways. He can tell you how steel foundries are making marvelous new nickel alloys that are used in the best crankshafts and valves in engines. He might become a fine engineer—if he were not subtly and invisibly handicapped by perceptual dysfunctions somewhere in the circuitry of his brain.

Some of his teachers have said Tom is just a little lazy and not willing to study hard enough to get the work. One teacher said partly in jest but with peculiar deeper bias, "Tommy become a mechanic? Whoever heard of an expert mechanic or engineer out of a kid who hasn't tried to learn to read any better than he does?"

Because of his perceptual-motor difficulties, the boy has never rated very well on the group tests used in his school. Such tests penalize many boys and girls like Tom. His top thinking abilities really are above average, but his best group-test rating when he was fourteen last year was 78—*borderline intelligence.*

Many Toms and Lauries are struggling along in our schools, often with no one sensing their real predicaments and feelings. Laurie never was a behavior problem at home or in school, and Tom presents no outward signs of his secret discouragement with himself. It has never been that great a problem to him.

"Anybody who can't read any better than I do must be dumb," he said with a sad finality one day when we were just talking at lunch time in school. He had asked me what I was doing in the school that day, and I had said I was checking some students who were not getting along very well in reading subjects.

These boys and girls with only slight signs of perceptual-motor dysfunction make up a large proportion of the school population in any community.

While these children may not show as clear signs of the basic difficulty as other children with more pronounced disturbances, the same general clinical picture can be noticed in many cases. Somewhat as in more severe cases, as noted in the first chapter of this book, the child may show:

——*some distractibility,* though usually mild and not as disruptive as in more severe disturbances. The teacher may simply wonder why the child at moments seems to be slightly *inattentive,* or why he is attracted to extraneous stimuli. This mild sign may go nearly unnoticed, unless the teacher is aware of its inferences about the child's neural makeup.

——*mild motor disinhibition,* perhaps no more than slight but chronic wiggliness.

——*some figure-background disturbances,* with mild difficulty in separating important aspects of a picture, sentence, or thought from the general background.

——*mild tendency to perseverate,* and hang on to a pattern of

110

behavior when changing to another. This sign is uncommon in mild cases, however, though in itself it is not a clear signal of severe disturbance.

— *some distortion of perception,* as though the eyes (and/or ears) were not quite doing their job accurately. The basic trouble is not really in the eyes (or ears) but in the cortical or subcortical areas of the brain that must do the seeing (hearing).

— *slight distortion of self-concept,* perhaps as though he sees himself immaturely.

— *occasional confusion in laterality,* perhaps viewed just as *immaturity,* but still enough to disturb reading, writing, arithmetic processes, and other school tasks.

These signs may be so mild in a particular child that they will go either unnoticed or else be dismissed as inconsequential. I can recall many boys and girls with mild perceptual-motor troubles that had never been suspected until high school, where these children suddenly were floundering.

"Why is he failing now in seventh grade?" parents and teachers have asked. "He used to have passing marks in lower grades. Has something suddenly pulled down his intelligence? Isn't he trying as hard as he did last year? Maybe what he needs is a sharp talking to, to let him know he can do the work if he wants to do it and works hard enough . . . ."

It is easier to label such a youngster as lazy and inattentive than to look at him long enough—and carefully enough—to fathom the real trouble and come up with effective ways to help him do better. This task swiftly separates truly great educators from less inspired and inspiring teachers. Careful diagnosis still is the key to helping all children who are having difficulty in school. Children with minimal signs of perceptual trouble are no exception to this rule.

Many errors of diagnosis come from doing *too little* with the child to check the symptoms—often through feeling too rushed to give more time to the job. Yet I have seen just as many errors of treatment come, paradoxically, from doing *too much*

111

15-year-old Jessica had been seen in several guidance service centers for children with school troubles. The first time she was nine and in third grade. The teacher said the child "probably could read much better if she would just settle down to such tasks instead of being so fussy most of the day." The art teacher took special interest in Jessica in fifth grade, noting that the child "seems to have perceptual difficulty . . . ." When Jessica was seen at 15 1/2, she showed many of the psychological signs found in children with cerebral injury. Her birth had been a very difficult breech presentation. She was very hyperactive as a baby. Early childhood years before school had included many sudden temper tantrums and vomiting spells. "Jessica surely was a nervous child," her mother recalled, "and very cranky at times, with no cause that we could see." Here are reproductions of her drawings of a man and a dog, when she was 15 1/2:

Rrover is a Rrendly dag

("Spelling always is hard for me!")

Some aspects of these drawings reflected subtle psychosis-like facets of her personality, as well as perceptual-motor difficulties. Jessica is over twenty now, but has shown no other signs of clinical psychosis. She earns a good income as a waitress in a busy diner.

Children's handwriting often reveals much more than how well they can spell. Jack at twelve gives few signals anymore that he sustained a severe head trauma in a bad fall when he was six. He has excellent health now, and gets along quite well with other boys his age. His handwriting, spelling, and arithmetic are below par, however, and he has considerable reading trouble some days. When the teacher asked the class to write a paragraph about their vocational ambitions, Jack tried hard to do it:

When I am order I want to be etheora balrnist or boulgist

65% actual size

Valerie is in the same class with Jack. She is twelve and also aspires to a career in science. She reads easily, and has no arithmetic difficulty. Her full-scale WISC IQ matches Jack's, 94, but her marks are much better than his. She began the paragraph:

When I am older I would like to be a scientist

65% actual size

with the child without surveying the results at intervals—again, through being hurried or feeling pressed to have an answer or get results. Snap judgement about a youngster, however *executive* it may sound, still is dangerous.

This is especially true in cases of children who show only faint signals of jittery feelings and difficulties in perception. Good teachers who have an inventive or experimental flair can adapt the kinds of tests that were discussed in the previous chapter to check children who may have *subtle imperception problems* underlying their mild school disabilities.

Caution must always be exercised in considering these children, to take time to look for signs of anxiety also. Anxiety can disturb a child's perception somewhat at times. An emotionally upset boy or girl may not be able to give careful attention to the task at hand, or keep at the job steadily enough and long enough to complete it well.

Worry about personal problems can defeat a child's attempts to study quietly and effectively. The youngster who is discouraged or fearful can hardly be expected to do his best on a test. An alert teacher with at least a few years experience in the classroom should be able to discern the usual signs of disruptive anxiety or fear in a child. Postponing the testing to a day when the child feels happier and more secure is wise in these instances. This avoids the clouding effects from emotional stress that would invalidate the child's test performance.

Thoughtful teachers know from experience in their own lives that a child's anxiety and irritability can have roots in the way others are trying to help him. Physicians tactfully use the adjective *iatrogenic illness* in saying that something in the treatment program is adding to the patient's illness, perhaps even causing the illness. The wise physician and nurse keep this possibility firmly in mind, in trying to help anyone who is sick. An overanxious teacher (or parent) often has induced discouragement and self-defeating behavior in the youngster.

This is not intentional of course, but it is easy to do, especially when the child is hypersensitive to signals of apprehension, fear, discouragement, or subtle hostility in the grownups who are involved with the problem. Maybe there ought to be special words in our vocabulary, to match *iatrogenic illness,* but to mean *school-induced* or *home-induced* illness. There are many upset and disturbed children in almost every school and community who could be so described medically. We might employ Greek again, in *scologenic* and *oikiogenic.*

Exactly what some children perceive who have even slight perceptual-motor disturbances is not easy to imagine. Nor is it a simple matter to guess whether most of the trouble such a child experiences is based somewhere in the afferent nervous system, the efferent system—or both. These puzzles are not easily answered, in any child. Eleven-year-old Robert is a case in point.

He is a happy boy; open, secure, hardly upset emotionally. In school he tries hard to do the job, but he is *barely passing* in spelling, arithmetic, and geography. Sometimes he seems *just below grade level* in reading, but his comprehension is much poorer. He can recall only part of what he has just read.

The art teacher suspected Robert's deeper trouble when she asked the boy to come a little early one morning for a special test. The boy came in a pleasant attitude, so she asked him to reproduce several simple figures, first from recall after a few seconds exposure, then by copying them in view, and then by tracing them on thin paper.

Children who show such signs, however slight, need the very best teaching techniques that can be devised, to try to circumvent at least part of the organic sources of troubles. At the same time, these youngsters usually need wise encouragement to be willing to keep working at the necessary tasks.

Such special hope must be based in reality at the same time, or it will soon wane into darker discouragement and self-depreciation than before.

The actual cerebral insult that caused damage (and now subtle dysfunction) in a particular child's case may have been

116

Here are two sets of Robert's drawings, grouped for better comparison of his perceptual-motor difficulties:

Figure shown	Recalled	Copied	Traced

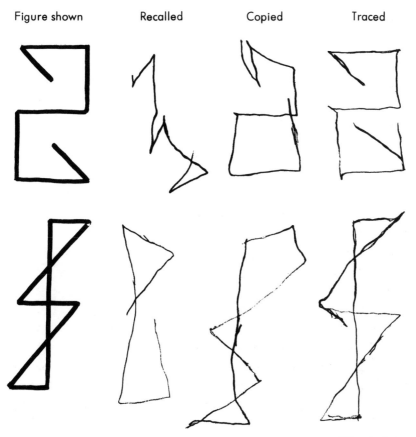

70% actual size

so slight that it left no *plainly* discernible neurological signs. For this reason it is unwise to use the phrase brain injury or damage about a child. A better term is that the child shows perceptual-motor disturbances.

Children faced with such trouble, however mild, need special help to get along well in school. Without the right understanding *and help,* they rarely come near their potentials. All children, perceptually impaired or not, show wide variations in personality characteristics as well as in abilities. Experienced teachers know this, and are not surprised when a boy or girl does not match the mythical *norm* for this particular age.

With jittery children it is always advisable that the learning environment be simple and routine. Reducing any unnecessary stimuli lowers the chance of distraction and enables these children to give more attention to important matters.

Any technique that makes the child's learning material stand out in bolder relief from the background, will enable him to manage it better. The more perceptual difficulty he experiences —visually, auditorially, tactually—the bolder the relief must be to help him most. Here is where the teacher's inventiveness and experimental-mindedness are invaluable.

Even children with only mild perceptual difficulties benefit by the right structuring of the classroom environment. This need not be rigid management, administered autocratically with little consideration for the fact that these children still need a warm sense of participation in establishing the controls and structuring. Here again is where the teacher's wisdom about children is a priceless ingredient in the situation.

Because these children, even in mild cases, so often are emotionally fluctuating and labile, they also are very sensitive to threat of failure. *This makes them react very cautiously and guardedly to whatever they perceive as "dangerous," "new," or "likely to expose them to failure."* The teacher who keeps this quietly in mind is in a far better position to work with these boys and girls. Pop quizzes, for example, or sudden changes in the classroom schedule or routine, can toss some of these children into very panicky behavior.

Many of these boys and girls feel quite insecure and confused about themselves. One very bright but very jittery 11-year-old said he felt very hopeless about himself. "I know I'm supposed to be bright enough, and I do feel a little better about myself than last year. But just look how poor my spelling still is!" With medication, he no longer showed such flighty distractibility as he had the year before, but his spelling still was poor—and he was well aware of this. Only the teacher's warm encouragement and support carried him through this stage. In junior high, without such support and understanding, he floundered badly for a long while.

These children greatly need—*and will accept*— the right kind of *disciplined routine.* This need often far excedes that of normal children who are not neurally involved, jittery, or perceptually impaired. It is easy to overlook or neglect this fact with children who show only mild imperceptual difficulties.

Taking off the needed controls and urging these children to work as impulsively as they please completely misses the point regarding their hyperactivity and jittery feelings.

Assuming that these boys and girls simply need warm affection, and will calm down when they are loved and valued enough, misses the mark just as far. Overdisciplining and overcontrolling them, as though they are simply mischievous kids who inherently know how to behave better, is equally far from what these children must have to change and grow sensibly.

Any teacher (and parent) who has had much experience with children who are even mildly brain-injured or who show even slight perceptual difficulties knows how *intractable* such a girl or boy can be at times.

Children with even slight signs of cerebral difficulty need a *calming* atmosphere around them in the classroom to be able to settle down to effective learning. Carefully planned and ex-

119

pertly taught lesson-sessions outrank all gadgets and gimmicks with jittery youngsters.

When a warmhearted and wise teacher finds ways to help such children stay *glued together* long enough in the classroom, their learning gains often can be amazing—to everybody concerned!

8

ENDOCRINE DYSFUNCTION CAN UPSET SCHOOL ABILITY TOO . . .

Physicians who see many children have always been aware of the wide, though sometimes veiled, effects of endocrine imbalance or disorder on how a child behaves and learns. Alert teachers in many schools are coming to understand these children in this clearer light in the last few years. There is little doubt any longer, particularly among physicians who treat many school children, that subtle disorders or imbalances in the endocrine system can bring extensive learning difficulties in some cases.

This chapter is intended simply to scan some of the hormone *linkages* within organ-systems, and *between* organ-systems in the child, that can disturb learning if not working smoothly. Many of these linkages were unsuspected even a few years ago. This present decade has been witnessing such vast advances in the fields of biochemistry and endocrinology that a whole section of a modern medical library is needed to house the major studies and texts. This chapter belongs in this book which is addressed to thoughtful teachers who desire at least to know something about children who have to live with endocrine difficulties. It is not intended to be encyclopedic about such problems. That would take up several medical texts written by specialists in endocrinology.

The precision of structure and function of the simplest cell and fiber reflect the magnificence of nature. The intricate chemical capacities of the endocrine secretions that bathe, alert, channel, balance, and coordinate the nearly quarter-of-a-billion cells and fibers of a child to enable him to be alive would have been outside most scientific comprehension a century ago.

Leading biochemists now believe that the essence of our lives, *and our individualities,* lies largely in the radically different distribution patterns of the electron charges within the molecules that comprise our cells and fibers, and our fluids and secretions. Slightest changes or redistributions of these patterns can widely alter functions and reactions of the molecules, and thus bring alterations and repercussions in function and behavior all the way up the ladder to obvious personality changes. Yet by no means do all these new discoveries add up to a gloomy picture of subcellular electrochemical predestination. There are harbingers of good hope mixed right in with the discoveries of how we are made, and how we function within the electrochemical powers of the cells of our bodies. These same scientists are beginning to surmise ways and means to prompt these very cells to correct and revamp some of their functions enough to bring renewed health and better behavior. These hopes are not rising out of far-fetched imaginings, but out of firmly based research.

The old mind-and-body dichotomy that was so commonly accepted by many people has gradually lost meaning in the brighter light of careful research in neurology, biochemistry, pharmacology, psychology, and psychiatry. We are more ready now to see that a child's behavior, how he learns, and even his personality facets are outer indications of all the vast array of interfunctioning organ-systems. Minute shifts in balance and utilization of proteins, carbohydrates, and metals, for example, now are known to account for many of the variations that children show in alertness, intelligence, and comprehension.

Endocrine malfunctioning is not often self-evident in children, at least not to degrees where the girl or boy obviously needs the physician's examination and medical help. Disturbances of some of the endocrines may cause greater difficulty than others for a child. Disorders of the thyroid, the hypophysis (also called the pituitary), and the pancreas sometimes bring marked changes in a child's personality, behavior, and general progress in school.

All the glands in the endocrine system, however, are intimately interlinked, both directly through the arterial system and indirectly through the nervous system. The complexities of many of these finely sensitive alerting, calming, balancing, and counterbalancing relationships are just beginning to be understood. Still others are just beginning to be suspected.

The next fifty years probably will encompass marvelous gains in such knowledge and its applications to many children. Even the present fund of information about the endocrines and their secretions can be helpful in keeping us more mindful of how intricate even the happiest and well behaving child really is. The following discussions of endocrine functions and some of the problems inherent in dysfunction are intended simply to be a broad overview. The order of discussion has no meaning here; each endocrine has its own importance of functions in the body. Each, in its particular ways, is paramount to life and health.

Thyroid

This endocrine gland has two lobes that are joined in an H-shape by a narrow band of tissue, called the isthmus. The gland hugs the lower portion of the thyroid cartilage in front of the neck. The shield-like form of this cartilage is the reason for its name: Greek, *thyreos,* shield; *eidos,* form. The tissue of the thyroid gland is yellowish red, about two inches high at the tallest points of the lobes, and about two inches wide. In most adults, the gland weighs about an ounce.

Before 1890, very little had been discovered about the thyroid and its functions. Its pad-like appearance in the neck of many women had led to a belief that the purpose of the gland was to beautify the neck region. In fact, a few years ago in some inland countries where the thyroid of many women was enlarged beyond its normal size, people were inclined to regard the enlargement as an enhancement to beauty. Now we would hope the physician and surgeon could remedy such a goiterous situation before severe harm had been done to the body systems. Effective treatment of children with thyroid difficulties now is quite commonplace, but there still are too many youngsters with such trouble who are struggling along unrecognized and thus untreated.

The thyroid's secretion, *thyroxin,* contains four iodine atoms per molecule. The actual quantity of iodine stored in the normally functioning thyroid is very small, yet this tiny amount has very important effects on the well-being of the individual. Even slight disturbances in the functioning of the gland soon may reflect in noticeable changes in personality and behavior. In some youngsters, these changes or difficulties have been widely misinterpreted by parents and teachers until a physician's sharper insight was sought.

Just how underfunction (hyposecretion) and overactivity (hypersecretion) of thyroid hormone brings the changes seen in some cases is as yet far from completely understood. The exact role of the iodine atoms of the molecule—and the electron charge distribution through this minute molecular structure—is still eluding biochemists. They are working hard on these problems, however, and one of these days some answers will be forthcoming.

We do know that the trace-amount of iodine in our daily diet is critically important to health and vitality. In inland areas, where iodine is exceedingly rare in the general diet, the incidence of goiter in children and adults is much higher. Inclusion of deep-sea fish and iodized salt (salt with the iodine simply left in it) can greatly diminish the number of children and grownups with goiterous conditions.

In recent years, biochemists have been suspicioning a much

wider role of thyroxin in the body's complex organ and nerve systems than just raising or lowering the basal metabolism rate of various tissues. The hormone probably has controlling and balancing roles in general growth, bodily proportion, intellectual development, and sexual development. Clearer answers will be coming out of new research in the next decade, for many able biochemists are working at these tasks.

Children with *hyperthyroidism* (overproduction of thyroxin) often show such signs as rapid pulse, very warm and moist skin, fine tremor of the hands, and protrusion of the eyes. Appetite may increase markedly, yet weight may decrease. The child may complain of feeling very tired and very weak. A thoughtful teacher can imagine how such problems may make the boy or girl behave poorly, and find increasing difficulty in school.

Irritability and touchiness are common in these children. There may be excessive restlessness, along with apprehension and anxiety. Sometimes the clinical differentials between hypothyroidism and possible brain damage are very difficult to discern.

Other children may suffer from *hypothyroidism* (undersecretion of thyroxin). This condition may bring oxygen starvation that can hamper some brain areas, so that the child does not develop normally mentally. Physicians have been able to help young children with this disorder by administering thyroxin. Biochemists may even discover ways to correct this condition in babies early enough to prevent major damage.

Parathyroids

These are four little endocrine glands, two on each side, partly imbedded in the rear surfaces of the thyroid lobes. Earlier anatomists and physicians thought the parathyroids were simply part of the thyroid gland. With the advent of thyroid surgery, the highly specialized nature of the imbedded parathyroids became dramatically apparent.

If the parathyroids were harmed greatly or removed, severe general muscle spasms soon developed, with death following swiftly. The muscle spasms were very much like those seen in patients where the calcium ion concentration in the blood stream had dropped to a low level. In animals that were deprived of the parathyroids, the throat muscles sometimes shut down so tightly that death came from asphyxiation. By 1915, surgeons had become exceedingly careful not even to touch a parathyroid with an instrument. Now, thyroid surgery is done quite safely, though always with special care and skill.

Parathyroid hormone (parathormone) now appears to regulate the amount of calcium ion concentration in the blood. This calcium is essential to proper blood coagulation, and proper functioning of nerves and muscles. Thus the parathyroids are in vital control of the whole skeleton and musculature. Excessive bone breakage sometimes is a signal of hyperparathyroidism.

Hyposecretion of these glands can bring muscle tone disturbances that might seem much like epilepsy or cerebral palsy. Such a child needs the wise insight, diagnosis, and care of an experienced physician. Prognosis generally is quite favorable, when the medical treatment is carried out along with good general hygiene and a nourishing diet. In most cases, the physician prescribes calcium and parathormone as an active part of the treatment.

Hypophysis Cerebri

This is also known as the pituitary gland. The name, hypophysis cerebri, comes from the Greek and means *growth beneath the brain*. Actually, the gland has two separate lobes that have no connection with each other functionally. Together, they are cradled in the sphenoid bone depression in the base of the skull, beneath the brain. Each lobe secretes vitally important hormones into the blood stream. Some of these hormones already are recognized, but several others are suspected to exist.

The anterior (frontal) lobe of the gland secretes at least six highly complex hormones. One of these is known as a *thyrotrophic* hormone (from the Greek for *thyroid-stimulating*) be-

126

cause it stimulates the thyroid gland. This mutual feed-back of the thyroid and anterior pituitary thus maintains many aspects of the healthy interorgan-system balance we have come to expect in ourselves and our children. We rarely stop to think that all these fine regulatory balances and counter-balances are miracles in themselves. Hyperthyroidism could arise out of improper functioning of the anterior hypophysis, though the apparent cause might seem to be in the thyroid itself. The physician must be highly skilled as an endocrinologist in such cases, to be able to discern the real trouble and know how to treat it properly.

Since 1940, anterior pituitary secretions have been recognized to have extensive somatotrophic (Greek: *body-nourishing*) properties, particularly affecting growth. Teachers who have worked with children who have grown too fast or too slowly know something of the concurrent personality, behavior, and learning problems that often are seen in such boys or girls. Listlessness can be so marked that the youngster may be judged as quite retarded. Motor coordination may be poor enough to make the child seem to be putting on an act.

This anterior lobe also produces the special hormone that stimulates the cortex (outer) portions of the suprarenal glands, so they in turn produce their vital health-protecting corticoids. This particular secretion of the pituitary is called *adrenocorticotrophic* hormone (adrenal-nourishing), and has thus come to be known commonly as ACTH. Slight imbalances in production of ACTH can have many *psychological* effects in the way we behave or learn. Probably many children with subtle dysfunction of this pituitary lobe are going through life somewhat misunderstood.

The posterior (rear) lobe of the gland also manufactures several complex hormones. One of these, known as *pituitrin*, was recognized about twenty-five years ago. Pituitrin has at least three important functions on the body's organ-systems: It helps to regulate the fine balance between retention and expression of water, so we neither are flooded out nor languish in drought. It stimulates the blood vessels to contract enough to maintain the right blood pressure around the circulatory system. And when a baby is to be born, the same pituitrin hormone helps to induce the necessary contractions of the uterus.

Overproduction of pituitrin can bring very distressing disruptions of the body's intricate carbohydrate metabolism, with marked energy disturbances, especially in children.

Suprarenals

These are also called the adrenals. These two important endocrine glands are really atop the kidneys, hence deriving their name from the Latin for *above the kidney*. Each suprarenal is nearly three inches long, shaped somewhat like a small icebag on top of the kidney.

The cortex or outer part of each of these glands and the medulla or inner part differ greatly in cell structure and in function. In very primitive fish, the two portions are completely separate glands, while in man the cortex envelops the medulla. Little wonder that earlier anatomists, biologists, and physicians had not been very successful in figuring out some of the chemical puzzles about these glands in humans.

Since 1890, remarkable progress has come, however. The noted Japanese biochemist, Jokichi Takamine, by then was hard at the task of isolating a pure substance from the medulla that has since become known as *epinephrine,* from the Greek meaning *upon the kidney,* referring simply to the suprarenals themselves. Takamine discovered that the new substance, even in minutest quantities, could swiftly increase blood pressure. At the time, this discovery was a great breakthrough for medicine, opening new doors wider in the search for answers to how some organ-systems control, compensate, and balance one another.

Within the next year, two English physiologists, William Bayless and Ernest Starling, were able to show that epinephrine acts through the bloodstream—as a hormone—without the nerve communication. These were momentous discoveries.

Out of such research that proved that the endocrines are *inter*stimulating, through the common channel of the blood-stream, came the term *hormone,* from the Greek verb meaning *to arouse.*

Hypersecretion of the suprarenal cortex in children sometimes brings marked sexual development and precocity. These changes come through the combined interorgan stimulation of the anterior pituitary and the suprarenal cortex secretions on the testicles of the boy or the ovaries of the girl. Slight disturbances in these intricate networks of endocrines may produce very disturbing changes in a child's development, with behavior difficulties that can upset schoolwork too. One 10-year-old in fourth grade that I remember was so fretful when she began to menstruate that year that her schoolwork declined to barely passing levels.

Overproduction of the suprarenal cortex hormone can cause excessive obesity and increased hairiness in adolescents. Little imagination is needed to see how such a problem could upset teenagers greatly, or make them behave poorly in many school situations. Expert medical care can help most of these children, but early referral and diagnosis still are important to avert severe emotional and behavior complications.

Gonads

These are the testicles or the ovaries. Their inclusive name, gonads, stems from the Greek for *generator of life,* thus referring to the generation of ova or sperm cells.

The testicles also produce highly specialized hormones, called *androgens* (from the Greek meaning *male-producing*), that selectively promote the boy's masculine development. The ovaries produce their own variation of androgen. These female sex hormones are called *estrogens* (derived from the Greek for *excitement*). Estrogens and androgens are very much alike in chemical structure. In fact, both are produced by the testicles and the ovaries. By intricate chemistry now only beginning to be understood, the girl's endocrine system usually manages to get rid of enough of the androgens, and stimulate production of sufficient estrogens, so that she develops properly as a young woman. Similarly, the boy's system usually is able to accomplish the opposite endocrine chemistry, so that he emerges to sturdy manhood.

When these critical chemical schedules are disturbed in a boy or girl, personality upsets can occur that may disrupt schoolwork too. Thoughtful teachers know this, and are alert to such signals of trouble ahead. The *thymus* gland, located in the upper chest, in front of the lungs and above the heart, is now known to exert special hormone control to keep children from spurting into adolescent development too early, before other body systems and structures are ready for such changes.

Other Glands

Other glands in the body play equally dramatic and vital roles in health and development. The *pancreas,* situated in the abdomen behind the stomach, is an *exo*crine rather than endocrine, pouring *out* its pancreatic juice through a duct into the duodenum during digestion, to aid in this process. All this has been known for centuries, but it is only part of the story.

Scattered through the tissues of the pancreas are special cells that have been known as *islands of Langerhans,* since the able German anatomist, Paul Langerhans, reported his discoveries about them in 1869. These minute specialized cell-clumps range in number in some individuals from three hundred thousand to three million in others. Totally, these cells rarely comprise more than two per cent of the mass of the whole pancreas. Their total weight may be only one gram, so it is not hard to understand how they were unnoticed so long even by careful anatomists.

Now they are known to produce the strategically needed *insulin* that acts to manage the level of glucose in the bloodstream. This fine life balance is attained through an amazingly complex intersystem feedback and counterbalancing that still is not fully understood. We do know that even slight dysfunctions in the network may bring diabetic problems, with all

130

their dangers to life itself. The discovery and synthesis of *insulin*, to make it available in the necessary quantities, has meant that thousands of children and adults have found new life and safety from diabetes.

Good schools now have effective programs to discern early, every child who may be diabetic. Such a test made a tremendous difference to one third-grader in a rural school I used to serve as the psychologist. The child had been wetting many times a day for quite a while. Her distraught teacher had felt the cause might be "nervousness"—or perhaps "veiled aggression toward a very strict household." The school had not yet joined in the program to check all children for possible diabetes. The teacher was capable enough, and warmly interested in her children; but she had not suspicioned the excessive wetting as a signal of organic trouble. The little girl had been "having so much difficulty with school anyway" that the wetting problem might not have alerted many teachers to call the nurse or physician to help.

A now common urine tape-test did indicate the need for the physician's diagnosis and help. Examination of the child confirmed the suspicion of diabetes, and the child was placed on insulin treatment. That once seriously endangered little girl is much older now, and a happy young woman who enjoys a full and rewarding life. Insulin was the miracle-worker. The jittery little girl "who used to be so listless and so disinterested in learning and was so upset at times" had needed most of all a careful physical examination.

Most of us have seen so many children growing up from birth to young adulthood that we rarely notice some of the amazing transformations of mind and personality that are going on so subtly all the time in every youngster. The clearer *physical* metamorphosis that happens at puberty and on through adolescence sometimes makes us take notice of such radical changes. Yet how rarely do we truly notice the inner metamorphosis of *spirit* that is happening all the while too.

131

Occasionally, perhaps in some course on exceptional children that prompts excursions into neurology or endocrinology, we have to take time to consider how aberrations or changes in cells and fibers and organ-systems can cause children to be upset and jittery enough to do very poorly in school.

If we have to take such excursions often enough, we begin to see that there are no neatly compartmentalized trichotomies of body-mind-behavior, either in our children or in ourselves. And then clearer insight comes about all children and how they behave. Some of the research on endocrine dysfunctions in children is beginning to force complete rethinking of many psychological concepts that have been suspect for a long time in more scientific circles of education.

This chapter was intended to keep such avenues to rethinking wide open for every alert teacher and parent who may browse these pages. Solidly founded hints have been coming out of recent studies that subtle chemical and metabolic disturbances are the culprits behind much of what has been called mental disease. There are good signs that some of the able biochemists who are hard at work on these problems will discover ways to prevent—perhaps even cure—such disease in many cases.

9

SOME CENTRAL

NERVOUS SYSTEM

DYSFUNCTIONS . . .

The human brain and nervous system are remarkably well protected from many dangers. Fortunately for all of us—and especially for active children—the skull is designed to be a very sturdy box that can withstand most of the accidents of childhood.

The spinal cord and nervous system are, by nature, quite ruggedly installed in the body and not easily hurt by the usual wear-and-tear of living. Apparently we are intended to come through childhood and adolescence fairly intact and healthy! Even severe head injuries do not leave dreadful sequelae in most instances. And skilled neurosurgeons now are able to intervene in cases that a few years ago would have been thought beyond such help.

New drugs are coming into use by physicians as an aid in managing brain infections that used to leave great damage in many children. Better baby and child care, plus more effective medical and surgical techniques, are changing the old pictures of neurologic injury and damage. Yet there are dangerous diseases and disorders that can injure a child enough to bring difficult learning and behavior problems, as many parents have discovered.

There still are fences to fall off, toxins that can harm cells, and diseases that can destroy tissues. There still are birth dangers, for baby as well as the mother. Even before the baby is born, there are *in utero* dangers. Life is like that. Getting born and growing up has always been fraught with danger. With all the new knowledge, we have only begun in some ways.

The brain and nervous system are so complex that we still have far to go before the most skilled diagnostician can be certain in some instances whether a child's peculiar behavior reflects emotional disturbance or cerebral injury—or both. Physicians usually are cautious in interpreting the *absence* of clear neurologic signs in a child who presents some learning problems or behavior difficulties.

Present methods of testing for organic brain pathology simply are not sufficiently sensitive to say absolutely whether a particular child has sustained such damage or is suffering from such a disorder. Experienced physicians remember that many children whose behavior cannot be explained by the medical history or neurologic examination may still have sustained brain disorder or damage not yet recognizable from the presently employed neurological signs.

Intensive research now going on in several university centers is opening even wider possibilities of *where* the dysfunction can be that is causing subtle perceptual distortion or disturbance in some children. Biologists are discovering that peripheral receptor cells—such as in the retina—are themselves highly complex, with many *pre-brain* functions of *discrimination*. The impulses reaching cortical areas in the brain from these peripheral receptors are already vastly different from simple undifferentiated *on-off* signals.

In this light, the whole nervous system is an intricate extension of the brain itself, with these far-flung outposts themselves marvelously organized to *sort out* incoming stimuli and send along impulse-information that is already partially comprehended, to the cortex. This new concept of the total nervous system and brain is upsetting some of the earlier and simpler concepts that have been widely accepted.

Discoveries in the next few years may support hypotheses now thought quite possible by many scientists: that highly complex and presently unsuspected *subtle* electrochemical imbalances and disorders of receptor cells may account for many of the perceptual difficulties some children show. Certainly there is increasing clinical evidence that some of the common infections that are so prevalent in young children may damage brain tissue in ways that have not generally been public knowledge.

Measles is one of the diseases that probably has injured many children. It is so contagious that few children have escaped in some communities. In many cases, particularly where parents do not recognize the symptoms, the child may seem to have "just a mean cold with a rash from the fever. . . ." There is little if any natural immunity to measles. Many children contract the infection twice, though some of the symptoms are not as plain after the first infection. Bronchopneumonia sometimes complicates measles and has often been fatal to the child. Otitis media, mastoiditis, and brain abscess are not rare with measles. Encephalitis is not as common, but can have damaging results to nerve fibers and cells.

So-called three-day or German measles—properly tagged *rubella,* in medical terms—is not as dangerous to the mother who comes down with it as it is to her unborn child. The peak danger period to the baby is within the early months of the pregnancy. Little hearts have been severely damaged, as well as eyes and ears. Head deformation from rubella has left children severely retarded mentally.

Regular measles can cripple and damage too, even when the infection has not appeared to be so deadly. About one child in a thousand develops encephalitis from measles. Most children who have measles recover well enough not to show obvious crippling. But Dr. Joseph Stokes, distinguished emeritus professor of pediatrics at the University of Pennsylvania School of Medicine, has warned that measles frequently leaves the child with lowered intellectual capacities as well as subtle motor difficulties.

These diminutions often go quite unnoticed in children, partly because teachers as well as parents simply are not aware of the changes in the child. A mother may say her child will be all right in a few weeks. "He was so sick he has a right to recover at his own rate."

The very bright youngster who had measles that infected the central nervous system may show some reduction in intelligence. Average children will be dragged down too, and not-so-capable children may be reduced to retarded levels. Marked alterations in the electroencephalograms of children before, during, and following rubella infections have been noted in many cases. These alterations reflect the serious danger of the disease even in cases that might seem mild enough to uninitiated persons. Dr. Stokes believes there may be a possible link between measles and severe behavior disturbances in many children. Cerebrally injured children who face increased trouble in school learning situations can become so discouraged that they are vulnerable to many kinds of delinquency.

This damaging disease could be wiped out in less than five years, Dr. Stokes has said, if all preschoolers were given vaccine. Several pharmaceutical firms now are producing measles vaccine, so that Dr. Stokes' long-hoped-for day when children will not suffer from this disease is at least in sight. This is truly one of the great scientific breakthroughs of the century, though it is happening with little fanfare in most communities. With America's birth rate now topping four million children for the tenth consecutive year, anything that can reduce the dangers of life to these youngsters is good news.

Recent studies have been throwing light on the effect of chronic anxiety and fear of the mother upon her unborn baby. Severe emotional turmoil can so disturb the complex internal chemistry of the mother that the uterus may tend to abort. Nearly ten per cent of mothers lose their babies in the early months of pregnancy. But at St. Luke's Hospital, in New York, 187 women who had suffered three or more miscarriages were given special care that strongly emphasized relief from fear

136

and anxiety. Eighty per cent of these women had successful deliveries.

Such programs should make us pause to think about the real possibilities of many children being born to mothers who needed such care but received only a small share of it. In an era that pours billions of dollars a year into surveying outer space, perhaps we need to invest far more in research and treatment of mothers-to-be, and of little children everywhere.

Just such a simple change as using a vacuum cup on baby's head, instead of the usual forceps, to help him be born is sparing many children and their mothers potential injury in many cases. With over four hundred babies delivered safely with the vacuum cup at Providence Hospital, in Washington, D.C., less than one per cent had lacerations like those that forceps can cause.

Some of the recent innovations in treating once-deadly disorders in new born infants are having marvelous results. In hyaline membrane disease, the stricken baby often dies in a few days because his immature body systems let too much water collect and clog his tiny lungs. Dr. Daniel Stowens, director of laboratories at Children's Hospital in Louisville, tried one remedy for this trouble: two epsom salt enemas administered to the baby immediately after birth. The epsom salt drew off the excess fluid so the child could breathe normally, sending the vitally needed oxygen to the brain and other tissues. (This particular treatment did not help in all cases, but physicians have been finding more effective measures that do work fairly well.)

There are new incubators for premature children, which reggulate body temperature within narrower range and thus insure far better starts in life for these babies. Today nine out of ten babies born with heart abnormalities are being greatly helped or cured entirely, by surgical techniques that would have been thought totally impossible a few short years ago. Surely these improvements and innovations are good news for everyone.

In light of this warm hope, we must still look squarely at the diseases and disorders that endanger the brains and central nervous systems of so many children. The following notes on some of these pathologies are not intended to be comprehensive. The list simply aims to alert thoughtful teachers to some of the terms physicians use in reference to cerebral dysfunction. The order of presentation does not infer the degree of danger that may be involved. Asterisks on some disorders or diseases call attention to the higher incidence among children in many communities.

Infections of the Meninges

The meninges are the sturdy membranes that cover the brain and spinal cord. Any infection of these membranes may seriously endanger the brain and CNS. Prompt diagnosis and effective medical treatment is imperative. Acute meningitis often involves such symptoms as violent headache, intense intolerance to sound and light, retraction of the head, convulsions, and coma, all reflecting the seriousness of the neurological involvement.

——*Acute purulent meningitis* would indicate a pus-forming infection of such microorganisms and destructive processes as:

Meningococcus (responsible for cerebrospinal inflammation).

Pneumococcus (there now are thirty-three known strains or types).

Staphylococcus (one of the wide Coccaceae family).

Streptococcus pyogenes (when given much headway).

Tubercle bacillus (causing tuberculosis).

Sarcoidosis (tumorous breakdown of meninges).

——*Subdural and epidural infections,* occurring beneath the dura mater. or on the outer surface of the dura mater. In either case, the infection may seriously endanger the brain or spinal cord inside:

Cerebral subdural empyema (pus formation in cavity).

138

Spinal epidural abscess of any kind, affecting the brain or spinal cord, or both.

*Brain abscess; such lesions are seldom primary, and usually result from severe infections of the middle ear, mastoid cells, and accessory sinuses. Brain abscess may also follow general septicemia, where the bacteria have invaded and are multiplying in the blood system. Severe lung infections with abscesses may spread to the brain.

—— *Virus infections,* particularly those causing such diseases as:

*Acute anterior poliomyelitis (an inflamed state of the anterior horns of the spinal cord).

Herpes simplex encephalitis, arising from so-called fever blisters that have established colonies in the brain via the blood system.

Herpes zoster when very severe; thought possibly to arise from filterable virus related to that causing chicken pox. An acute inflammatory disease of the skin, with pus vesicles usually distributed along nerve trunks.

Venereal disease that inflames, enlarges, or ulcerates the lymph glands, thus transmitting to the brain via the blood system.

Measles meningitis and encephalomyelitis, from severe measles infection.

Mumps meningitis and encephalomyelitis, from severe mumps infection.

Encephalitis lethargica (an infective disease that first was recognized in England in 1918); brain abscesses develop in many instances, with marked cerebral damage.

Hemorrhagic encephalitis (hemorrhage in the brain accompanying inflammation).

—— *Rickettsial infections* come from minute organisms found in:

Typhus fever.

Spotted fever (tick fever).

—— *Syphilis* invading any of the brain or nerve tissues may cause extensive damage with extensive deteriorative changes in intellect and personality.

——*Other microorganisms* known now to cause brain and CNS damage are:

Cerebral (or cephalgic) malaria.

Trichinosis, when ingestion of worms has been great.

Trypanosomes (a boring multitailed protozoa parasite that sometimes enters the blood stream and thus can reach the brain and CNS).

Vascular Lesions

A vascular lesion is any damage to the blood vessels. The brain and CNS, by the physical importance of their functions in the body, make special demands on the blood system to supply oxygen and other vital materials, and to carry off organic byproducts that otherwise would endanger the cells. Any damage or interruption to the arterial system that depletes an adequate blood supply to the brain and nervous system for more than a few moments may leave extensive damage or dysfunction that may still be partly reversible in some cases even after a long time.

——*Diseases of the cerebral blood vessels* have direct implications for the health and functioning of the brain as well as the CNS:

*Hemorrhage anywhere in the brain endangers the tissues and cells that are normally served by the blood vessels that are involved.

Cerebral thrombosis, a blood clot anywhere in the arterial system of the brain, can bring serious damage that may heal very slowly at best.

Cerebral embolism, a piece of foreign matter obstructing any of the arterial systems of the brain, can have equally serious results to intelligence and behavior. Nearly always embolism is caused by bacterial endocarditis (inflammation of the membrane that lines the heart). Some bacteria can infect and inflame this endocardium

140

so that small pieces may slough off and be carried in the blood supply to such places as the smaller vessels in the brain.

Hypertensive encephalopathy, noninfectious breakdown of brain tissues caused by marked rise in blood pressure, can damage vital areas seriously.

—— *Intracranial aneurysm,* dilatation of a weak place in the wall of an artery, caused by blood pressure, may damage surrounding brain cells by compression, as well as by the clot that may form in the distended artery, and thereby cut down the blood flow to brain areas. Hemorrhage danger is also present in these cases.

—— *Vascular diseases of the spinal cord* involve comparable dangers to the nerves in the cord, with implications for lowered intellectual functioning and general capacity:

Any infections or damage to the blood vessels supplying the spinal cord may have disasterous effects.

Myelomalacia, softening of the spinal cord, soon disrupts vital nerve circuits to organ-systems.

Hematomyelia, hemorrhaging of blood into the spinal cord, likewise can swiftly disturb and disrupt the nerves in the cord so they can no longer function as they should. Traumatic spinal injuries commonly involve this hazard.

*_Tumors_

Tumers anywhere within the skull take space the brain simply cannot spare. For a while, some brain areas can tolerate the pressure from a very small tumor, but even such tumors gradually give signs of trouble in disrupted and clouded behavior and performance. Surgery is beginning to offer the best hope in the following cases:

—— *Tumors of the skull* are relatively rare but still cause great trouble when they do occur. Some kinds of skull tumors are:

Hyperostoses are abnormal growths of bone tissue.

Osteomas, which are tumors of bone-like structure developing on bones or other tissues.

Hemangiomas, which are tumorous growths made up of dilated blood vessels.

Metastatic tumors, which are secondary malignancies arising at a distance from the primary growth.

—— *Tumors of the meninges* are often referred to as meningiomas in some medical parlance.

—— *Tumors of any of the cranial nerves,* such as:

Gliomas (malignant tumors) of the retina or optic nerve.

Neurofibromas (tumors of the connective tissue of a nerve).

—— *Gliomas* (malignant tumors) such as:

Astrocytomas, which are tumors of the connective tissues that form the supportive substance of the cerebrospinal axis or CNS.

Medullablastomas, which are granular tumors of the medulla oblongata of the brain, or of the spinal cord.

Oligodendrogliomas, which will damage the fine, vine-like structure of the brain and CNS.

—— *Tumors of the endocrine glands,* such as:

Pinealomas, which are tumors of the pineal body in the brain.

Pituitary tumors (tumors of the hypophysis).

—— *Congenital tumors,* particularly blood vessel tumors and malformations, are being corrected. Also tumors that affect or involve the functioning tissues of any vital organ, and thus may have adverse effects on the brain and CNS are being successfully treated.

Any tumors that invade the neural systems by metastasis (producing secondary malignancies), can be dangerous.

*Trauma

A trauma is a wound or injury, particularly to the brain and CNS. While these tissues are marvelously self-healing and self-repairing in many instances, any injury to them involves some danger to later function:

—— *Craniocerebral trauma,* when severe, may bring many complications later, even though at the time the person

142

seems to be recovering very well with no sequelae to the injury.

—— *Trauma involving damage to any of the arterial or fluid systems of the brain or CNS* may endanger these organs seriously.

*Developmental defects of the brain and CNS

—— *Congenital hydrocephalus,* in which disorder serous fluid collects in the head and thus exerts increasing pressure on the brain.

—— *Spina bifida* is a congenital defect in the walls of the spinal cord, so that the cord is pushed through the opening to form a tumor-like knot of nerve fibers. Prognosis is poor in most instances.

—— *Cranium bifidum* is a rare defect of the dura mater allowing the brain to herniate.

——*Malformations of the occipital bone and cervical spine,* particularly malformations of the atlas or first cervical vertebra that supports the head can be very harmful as well as any fusions of the cervical vertebrae that would thus cramp the spinal cord.

—— *Premature closure of the cranial sutures* will cause damage to the developing brain.

—— *Ocular hypertelorism* (abnormal width between the eyes) tends to present special visual problems in some cases.

—— *Cerebral palsy* is the loss of ability to control movement accurately, and is caused by a lesion of some part of the brain.

*Degenerative diseases
Degenerative diseases of the brain and CNS, stem in some instances from more general involvementst such as:

—— *Disorders of the lipoid (fat) metabolism.*

—— *Pick's disease* (sometimes known as Neimann-Pick's disease), involves progressive dementia.

—— *Tuberous sclerosis.*

—— *Primary degeneration of the corpus collosum* (interconnecting fibers in the brain).

—— *Paralysis agitans* (sometimes called Parkinson's syndrome).

—— *Diseases of the basal ganglia* which are the bundles of nerve tissues that receive and send out impulses from the brain. Included are Sydenham's chorea, and chronic progressive chorea.

—— *Gargoylism* and the *Mongolian* syndrome usually involve intellectual retardation ranging from mild to severe.

*Cerebellum diseases, such as:

—— *Hereditary cerebellar* (and spinal) *ataxia* and muscular incoordination due to brain disease or damage. Spasticity is often part of the clinical picture; sometimes there is muscular atrophy also, in varying degrees.

—— *Cerebellar deterioration* or degeneration.

*Spinal cord diseases, such as:

—— *Sclerosis.*

—— *Spastic paraplegia* (usually familial).

—— *Syringomyelia,* which is the development of cavities within the spinal cord.

*Neuromuscular disorders, such as:

—— *Progressive muscular dystrophy.*

—— *Hypertrophic interstitial neuritis.*

Diseases arising from toxins

Toxins are poisonous substances or compounds, such as:

—— *Bacterial toxins,* such as diphtheria, tetanus, and botulism.

—— *Metallic poisons,* including arsenicals, bismuth, lead, manganese, mercury, and thallium.

—— *Organic compounds,* such as ethyl alcohol, methyl alcohol, barbiturates, belladonna, bromides, hydantoins (from urea or allantoin), and carbon monoxide.

144

Metabolic diseases and dysbalances

These may impair and disrupt functions of the brain and CNS and include:

——*Endocrine system diseases,* of the pituitary, thyroid, parathyroids, adrenals, and pancreas, so that the gland does not secret the proper amounts of hormones to maintain good body health.

—— *Diseases of the blood,* such as primary anemia, sickle cell anemia, and polycythemia (overproduction of red cells).

—— *Diseases of the bones,* such as Paget's disease (where long bones of legs, hip bones, and skull may deform gradually).

—— **Polyneuritis,* such as occurs from severe vitamin deficiency, ingestion of arsenicals or lead, diabetic breakdown, diphtheric infection, or lesions from Hansen's bacillus (leprosy).

Demyelinating diseases

These injure the protective sheath (myelin) of the nerves, and can markedly disturb all nervous functions. Such diseases include:

—— *Multiple sclerosis.*

—— *Schilder's disease,* which is usually diffuse in effect.

—— *Acute encephalomyelitis.*

—— *Neuromyelitis of the optic nerve.*

—— *Progressive subcortical encephalopathy.*

Diseases and functional disturbances of as-yet-unknown etiology

These unknown factors can mask and disrupt brain and CNS function. Such diseases and disturbances include:

—— *Convulsive disorders,* such as:

Tetany, which is a nervous disorder with intermittent tonic spasms. It is thought to be caused by parathyroid deficiency. Thyroidectomy may induce a serious form of the disorder.

Epilepsy. Some epileptics have been found to have a scarred area of the brain attached to the cranium. Surgery has corrected the situation. Myoclonic forms of the disorder may be mild, with twitching or clonic spasm of a muscle group.

Carotid sinus syncope, which is fainting caused by a suddenly lowered blood supply in the principal artery of the neck.

——*Myasthenia gravis,* which causes great muscular weakness without atrophy. The prognosis is generally grave. Intellective and personality changes are usual.

——*Psychoses and psychotic-like mental disturbances.*

The specific prognosis for cerebral involvement or damage in any of these conditions depends, of course, on many intricate factors. In many places now, well-trained physicians and clinical psychologists are teaming up to combine their skills in discerning these children early and helping them get around at least part of the trouble.

The list has been included in this chapter simply to acquaint teachers and other interested persons with some of the hazards of living that children can face and frequently survive, with remarkable stamina and self-healing powers!

Lee has been a wonderful example. He is twelve now, and doing so much better in school that the improvement has seemed almost miraculous. Perhaps it has been, in the real sense of the phrase. The improvement certainly has been quite beyond what had been expected when Lee was a little boy of two or three. He is one of scores of children I have known clinically since they were preschoolers. I have had an excellent opportunity to study these youngsters over many years. These special children in my case files have increased my hopes about many others with cerebral difficulties.

Lee had a very rough time at birth. Labor was long and traumatic for mother and infant. The baby needed oxygen for several days, and there were signs even then of diffuse cerebral

injury. Little Lee was a very hyperactive baby, somewhat convulsive, perhaps from the mother's eclampsia (major toxemia)
before the birth. Hospital records noted blood in the baby's
spinal fluid, a signal of probable injury to the brain at birth.
The child certainly had a rough start in life.

When Lee was three and a half, his parents were having so
much trouble with him that they were willing to try any advice. And, as in most such cases, advice rolled in from every
source.

"You ought to spank that child, let him know who's boss."

"Play with him more, he needs to know he's loved and valued."

"Have a new baby, to take your minds off Lee; he's too much
   the center of things in your house."

"Every time he pulls those tricks, spank him harder."

"Have you thought about putting Lee in the new nursery school
   over in So-and-so? The teachers are excellent, I hear."

"You ought to take Lee to our family doctor; he's helped our
   children so much."

("Those parents are the ones who need the most help! I could
   straighten out that boy in a hurry if he lived in our house a
   few weeks.")

The nursery school managed to keep Lee two months, and
then suggested that the children's mental health center, in a
nearby city, might be able to help. The center said Lee could
be seen in about seven months, so the parents felt frustrated
even more. "Let's try anything to make the child behave better,
we simply must do it, how will he ever be ready for school
next year if we don't?"

At this point the family physician asked me to consult with
Lee's parents about the boy. They brought him to the office
and it did not take long to understand why they had felt so
upset. In the first few minutes Lee managed to tangle up the
secretary's typewriter by pressing several keys at once. He re-
adjusted all the venetian blinds in three rooms. The new recorder spilled out about ten yards of tape at high speed. All
the office intercoms were buzzed. Lee's father captured the boy

upstairs, in the speech clinician's room, where the child had swiftly scattered all the toys in every direction. *Hyperactive* did not sound like the word the secretary was saying about Lee just then.

But *hyperactive* seemed to describe the child very clearly to me, along with *probably superior intellect; swift in comprehension; not an angry child who feels unloved or frightened; and certainly not lacking in energy or investigativeness.*

Lee started first grade just before he was six. He has always been a handsome child, with a ready smile and an alertness to all around him. But the teacher gradually felt that Lee "must be retarded; he seems completely unable to retain what he learned a day or two before. He will be passed to second grade only because our superintendent insists that no child be held up or put in special class until fourth grade." Probably the real reason Lee reached second grade was that he was so hard to manage. One year was enough for any teacher. "When that child is out sick, the whole class behaves better," the teacher said one day.

The parents were ready to admit an impasse and let me make an appointment at a children's center for an electroencephalogram and thorough medical examination. The trip and services cost a few dollars, but the money was well spent.

The neurologist found some signs of earlier cerebral injury, and the encephalogram pointed to the same difficulty. The EEG basic frequency was 9 to 11 per second, with fairly normal amplitude for a child Lee's age. However, very disorganized occasional sharp wave activity was quite marked, at bicentral and right posterior regions. When Lee was asked to breath very deeply (hyperventilation), this produced a swift and marked buildup in the electrical activity, with bilateral bursts and runs of very high voltage, and then very disorganized slowing. Frequent slow wave and slow spike activity occurred at posterior regions. Photic stimulation (with a flashing neon lamp, controlled for certain frequencies) produced low voltage single spike activity at left frontal-central regions.

Lee's record was interpreted by the physician-specialist in electroencephalography on the center's staff. The record seemed definitely abnormal, reflecting considerable cerebral dysrhythmia. The record was not as clear diagnostically as some children's are, but it was quite compatible with a major convulsive disorder. All this fitted the general picture Lee had been presenting in school and at home.

The family physician decided to try Lee on medication to help the boy feel less anxious and jittery. In a few weeks the change in Lee was remarkable. Meanwhile, his mother and father were helped to *get off their own backs* and to understand the real cause of much of Lee's hyperactivity and poor school showing which was organic brain difficulty, rather than too much love and permissiveness or not enough of these.

Lee, much calmer by this time, was happier in school too. He became less of a problem there and was able to attend better and for longer periods. He came to the office and I used the WISC and several other test techniques to reevaluate his improved capacities. The new teacher in September was interested in Lee, and followed my suggestions on how to get him down to learning to read. He actually gained a year in about eleven months.

Perceptually he still had many problems, and the art teacher often noted how poorly Lee drew, even when the boy appeared to be doing his very best. Writing was so difficult that we tried another approach to circumvent the obvious motor incoordination: a typewriter. This turned the tide for Lee; he found he *could* get down on paper what he had in mind.

He is twelve now, has a warmhearted and skilled teacher, both in the *regular* class group for half a day, and in one of the fine special classes in his school for the other half day. He is proving he is a very bright lad. He likes to read, particularly books about new engines and aircraft.

He needs little special medication anymore and sleeps quietly now, with none of the night-terrors he used to have. His mother says there have been no rough emotional episodes all year. Best of all, the old moody discouragement has gone.

He likes to call or write to me occasionally. These letters have helped him want to read and write better. Here is a note he typed recently. Notice the kinds of errors that still reflect a little of the old perceptual-motor-expression problems he used to face:

```
How are you?        Two weeks ago I was vrey

sick, the flu I guses but now I feel much better.

 I joined our basket ball team  I do very well wiht it.

We built a garage the job was fun.  Do you rembrer our

old Desoto?  We are going to take the odl engine from

it.  We are not realy waisting it beacuase theres no

rervesre init.  XXXX  This year I hope to get a new

treblo trian for my birhtdy.  I like myteachrer this

year, she helps all the kids, we like her.  Getting

back to the grarage I helped with the job and my

grandfather says I can do amans job.  Keep well and

write to me when you get tmie.

                        Your friend,

                             Lee
```

By their nature, the human brain and nervous system are certainly not indestructible. Yet by this very same nature, they have marvelous self-healing and self-reestablishing power.

10

MOST FAMILY DOCTORS NOW CAN SPOT CNS TROUBLE IN CHILDREN . . .

It is so easy to be fearful *and resistant* about anything we do not understand or have never experienced in our own lives. Apparently it is very human to be *down on* whatever we are not *up on* by training or experience. This fact of life at least partially explains why some parents—and some teachers—show panic when a child needs to be seen by a neurologist.

One mother blanched at the suggestion and said her child had never seemed psychotic to her. Gentle questioning revealed some of her deeper fears that the physician would drill a hole in the child's head and put some kind of wires inside to shock the child. This mother had an even wilder concept of what a psychiatrist does in examining and treating a child.

Such misconceptions probably are much wider spread than generally thought. Most parents have a secret abhorrence of anything that even vaguely implies some kind of nervous system dysfunction. Fortunately, this picture gradually is changing, as more teachers (and parents too, in many communities) are beginning to see that the earlier a child is *accurately diagnosed,* the earlier he can be helped by the right treatment.

This is just as true for children who may have suffered injuries of the central nervous system or brain as well as for children who may be suffering from other disabilities, injuries, or diseases. Good physicians know this, and call on the experienced neurologist in cases where symptoms seem to point to possible brain or CNS involvement.

The physician's special knowledge and skills enable him to examine a child thoroughly for symptoms of central nervous system dysfunction or damage. Many physicians now have expert knowledge and understanding of the intricate structure, function, etiology, and pathology of all the central nervous system, as well as the organ-systems of the body and their complex interactions. Such a physician recognizes the subtle signs of trouble anywhere along these system networks. These abilities make him a valued and indispensable member of the diagnostic team who have to understand and treat children with possible central nervous system damage.

He knows how much such lesions can complicate the diagnostic and treatment picture of children, especially in cases involving high blood pressure and other vascular diseases, diabetes, infections, and pernicious anemia. For this reason, he prefers to have an opportunity to study the detailed medical history of a child, with particular emphasis to the *presenting symptoms,* before he examines the child. Careful school records are a helpful part of the clincal picture the neurologist may want to read. The family history may give important cues too, in some cases.

The physician's examination has specific diagnostic purposes. He wants to determine whether the brain can and is functioning properly or not. If there are signs of malfunction anywhere, he wants to determine where the trouble is, and the kind and extent of the lesion that is causing the trouble. Then he must estimate the degree to which the healthy, unimpaired parts of the CNS can be utilized to enable the child to circumvent the difficulty.

This is no small task, even in the apparently *uncomplicated* case. The physician has to depend largely on an exacting examination procedure that carefully checks all the intellective, thinking, feeling, and reacting aspects of the child. He probably will ask for information about any difficulties the child has had with seizures, fainting, double vision, bladder or bowel control, or signs of increasing disability.

Personality changes or unconscious spells in the child will definitely interest the neurologist who is to examine the youngster. Whether the child is right or left-handed will have an important bearing on many of the tests. Some parents are surprised to learn that the neurologist ordinarily uses little specialized apparatus in the examination. His office may be quite similar to the office of the family physician. This is good, especially in cases where the child might feel jittery anyway about *going to the doctor.* Most doctors who work with children generally are expert at helping a child feel less afraid and tense. In most instances, the child may feel less upset by the neurological examination than a checkup for other purposes by the physician.

The examination procedure generally proceeds in steps, testing the nervous system functions from higher to lower levels of integration. The neurologist does not expect to make a conclusive diagnosis on the basis of the neurological symptoms alone, but only when these signals are corroborated by the broader physical examination signals. With this in mind, he may begin by carefully examining the child physically.

The following brief outline may interest teachers who have wondered how the physician goes about the neurological phase of examining a child:

Testing the child's general mental functioning
Are there any signs of general behavior defects?
Does the level of consciousness seem below normal in any way?
Does the child show intellectual difficulties or defects which can not be accounted for in light of his school and home background?

Are there signs of excessive tension, hostility, depression, or euphoria?

Are there any inappropriate or bizarre reactions?

Does the child seem very preoccupied with thoughts or ideas?

Testing the child's cerebral functioning more specifically

Are there any signs of sensory perception defects to touch, pain, temperature, body position, or vibration?

Are there any signs of difficulty in recognizing the form of solid objects by touching or handling them?

Does the child have difficulty in recognizing by touch simple figures or letters traced on his palms with a blunt instrument?

Does he have difficulty in understanding or in using words or gestures in communicating ideas?

Are there signs of trouble in remembering?

Does the child show defects in insight for his age and school level?

Does he have difficulty in orientation to himself and others, to where he is, or to time?

Does he seem to have delusions of any kind: false beliefs rising out of disturbed sensations?

Does he seem to have any hallucinations: perceptions without proper stimuli?

Testing his motor strength and reaction

Has the child been developing good lateral dominance of hand, foot, eye, and ear?

Are there any signals of strength defects out of line with the child's likely daily experience and medical history?

Are there any signs of muscle atrophy (wasting away)?

Are there tremors in any muscle systems at rest? In any muscle systems at work?

Is there any peculiar rigidity or contracture of muscles?

Does the child's muscular tone seem abnormal in any way?

Each of these subtests has special diagnostic inferences to the neurologist as he examines the child. Yet they may not take very long for him to carry out with a youngster. His keen mind can record the signals he is checking for in a few minutes. The child may even think the procedures are fun. The rest of the examination can be just as effectively carried out with most children. A thoughtful teacher scanning this outline probably will recognize many of the implications of the check points for understanding what may be the trouble in a girl or boy. The neurologist, of course, must have intimate and exact knowledge of such implications, to diagnose the trouble accurately.

Testing the child's cranial nerve functions

Olfactory nerve: With his eyes closed, can the child correctly identify familiar odors such as coffee, tobacco, cloves, and other odors that he should be expected to know? (The neurologist would first check for possible obstruction of the child's nasal passages.)

Optic nerve: Many studies are revealing as high a proportion as one child in every four of school age with faulty vision. The neurologist checks the youngster for visual acuity, extent of visual field of each eye, and any blind spots. He will make a careful ophthalmoscopic examination of each eye, to observe the optic disc, the vessels, and the periphery of the retina. He knows the optic nerve and the retina actually are an extension of the brain itself, so he inspects the eye realizing he is seeing right into the living brain.

Oculomotor, trochlear, and abducens nerves: These are usually tested as a group. They supply the muscles that move the eyes in various ways. The neurologist checks the child for signs of difficulty in smoothly following his finger in a large circle, in looking down-and-out, and in looking up-and-out. He will notice any complaints of double vision, and especially any nystagmus (constant involuntary movement of the eyeball). True nystagmus would reflect cerebral damage in most cases. The examination would include a check of the child's pupillary light reflexes. This also reflects nerve health or impairment.

Trigeminal nerve: This is the most difficult of all nerves to trace, but it now is known to serve surfaces of the face, tongue, and teeth. Checking intactness of this nerve is not a simple task. The neurologist may check the child's responses to light pinpricks of certain facial areas, and to warm and cold objects. The child's eyes are closed during these tests. Slight touch sensations must be checked on the forehead, cheeks, and jaw areas. The neurologist will be alert for any differences in response on opposite sides of the face. He will check the maxillary reflex by tapping the middle of the chin with a reflex hammer when the child's mouth is slightly open. The normal reflex is a sudden, slight closing movement of the jaw.

Facial nerve: This test usually amuses the child, because the neurologist asks the youngster to imitate him as he looks at the ceiling, wrinkles his forehead, frowns, smiles, and lifts his eyebrows. Any asymmetry of the child's face is a signal of possible nerve dysfunction. The strength of the eyelid muscles is tested simply enough by asking the child to try to keep his eyes closed as the physician attempts to open them with his thumbs. The sensory portion of the facial nerve is tested by asking the child to try to identify the taste of sugar, and then salt, placed on the front part of each side of the tongue as the child holds it out steady. (You can imagine why this test is hard to do with some children!)

Acoustic nerve: This nerve is divided into two parts. One serves the cochlea and the other serves the vestibule of the ear. If the child has a history of feeling very dizzy at times, of everything turning around, or of disturbed balance, there may be a lesion of the vestibular part of the nerve. The cochlear part is a little easier to check with several tests, including asking the child to tell how far away from the ear a ticking watch can be heard. The neurologist may check for lateralization by placing the base of a vibrating tuning fork on the middle of the child's head and asking him whether the sound seems to be centralized, or nearer to one side of the head. Much hearing loss in the child may indicate cochlear nerve damage at the pontomedullary junction in the brain.

Glossopharyngeal nerve and Vagus nerve: These are generally tested together. The glossopharyngeal nerve supplies the mucous tissues of the pharynx, soft palate and tonsils, and some of the adjacent areas. The vagus nerve supplies the motor fibers to the pharynx, larynx, and soft palate. The neurologist's tests of these nerves may include eliciting a gag reflex by touching each side of the pharynx with a tongue depressor or applicator stick. He may stroke each side of the mucous membrane of the uvula to see whether the touched side rises, as it should. If the child can swallow normally, speak clearly without hoarseness, and shows symmetrical movements of the soft palate when asked to say "ah," the vagus nerve is functioning normally.

Spinal accessory nerve: This nerve serves the large muscles of the neck and back, and is easy to check by asking the child to shrug his shoulders or turn his head against resistance by the physician.

Hypoglossal nerve: This nerve serves the tongue muscle exclusively. This makes it easy for the physician to check by asking the child to hold the tongue straight out, and then to move it from side to side against a tongue depressor. Signs of atrophy, tremor, and peculiar weakness are noted as reflecting possible nerve difficulty.

Now the neurologist can move along in the examination to the next step. He has been given a clear picture of the intactness and functional health of the child's nervous system. Whatever peculiarities or defects have shown up are, by now, beginning to give him increasing insight about the source of the difficulty somewhere along the nerves or in the brain. Of course he does not look alarmed or let the child know he has found any trouble. He knows this would be unwise and only complicate the diagnostic problem. If a bright and alert youngster asks why a certain test is used or what it means in his own case, the physician usually answers supportingly. "You're scoring all right, my boy, let's see how you can do this one. . . ."

Testing the child for cerebellar trouble

The cerebellum controls balance and coordination. The tests for intactness and health of the cerebellum include checks of the child's body balance and coordination:

First with eyes open, and then closed, can the child touch his finger to his nose, ear, eye, and knee?

With his eyes open, can he touch his finger to the physician's finger in several locations? Especially can the child do this quickly as the physician moves his finger. Each hand should be tested and any peculiar differences noted.

Can the child point to the physician's hand with the big toe, and make a figure 8 in the air with each foot?

Is the child able to stand erect with feet together, with eyes open and then closed, without much movement to keep balance?

With eyes open, does the child have good balance while he walks naturally?

Can he walk heel-to-toe, eyes closed, with fairly good balance?

Do the child's arms swing naturally as he walks around the room?

Testing the child's motor nerve system

The physician-neurologist probably will check the youngster's muscles, while at rest, for size, consistency, and possible atrophy. Peculiarities of symmetry of posture, and of muscle contours and outlines will be noted.

Do the child's fine muscles of each hand show any signs of wasting or fasciculation (forming little bundles)?

Do the hands show any tremors in the muscle fibers?

Are there abnormalities in the tone of muscles, such as spasticity, rigidity, or flaccidity?

Are there any unusual involuntary muscular movements?

Do the child's muscles show any unusual weakness?

Testing the sensory system

Here the phsyician carefully notes the child's ability to perceive the sensation being tested, especially comparing both sides of the body and corresponding extremities. He will check the child's sensitivity to various kinds of sensation, including sensitivity to a wisp of cotton lightly brushing the area, to a pinprick, to heat and cold, and to vibration.

Are the child's hands, forearms, upper arms, feet, legs, and body normally sensitive to light touch?

Are these same areas normally sensitive to the superficial pain of a pinprick?

Are these areas normally responsive to temperature sensations?

Are they sensitive to vibration?

Can the child reproduce motion and position of muscles that have been passively moved by the examiner?

Can he accurately discriminate two-point contact from single-point contact? Can he show where he was touched?

Can he discriminate textures such as cotton, wool, and silk, by feeling the materials with his hands?

Can he recognize simple letters or numbers traced on his palms or finger tips with a blunt point?

With his eyes closed, is the child able to tell that he has been touched on both sides of his body in identical areas, at the same time?

(These tests are aimed to reveal any disturbances of the cortical modalities of sensation. The neurologist would interpret such disturbances as reflecting possible involvement of the parietal lobe.)

Testing the child for his reflex status

These tests require extensive experience and skill. The neurologist-physician must do them very carefully, and take note of any peculiarities or imbalances of corresponding sides of the

body. There are many tests of the child's reflexes that can be performed in the examination. Here are the common ones:
Biceps reflex; to test intactness of cervical nerves 5 and 6.
Triceps reflex; to check cervical nerves 6, 7, and 8.
Patellar reflex; to test lumbar nerves 2, 3, and 4.
Achilles reflex; to check sacral nerves 1 and 2.
Upper abdominal; to test thoracic 7, 8, and 9.
Lower abdominal; to test thoracic 11 and 12.
Babinski reflex, to check for pyramidal tract diseases or damage. (This is one of the most valuable signs in neuropathology. It is elicited by stroking the lateral aspect of the sole of the foot. In pyramidal tract disease, the big toe extends strongly, in addition to the fanning-out of the rest of the toes. The test must be very carefully performed and interpreted, of course.)

In cases where the child is very anxious or jittery at the moment, the physician may have to postpone some tests he would like.to do. Any teacher who has worked with such youngsters can understand this, but parents sometimes find the situation provoking. Here is where the thoughtful teacher or school nurse can help to prevent such anxiety in the child by telling (and showing) him what the physician may do in the examination.

11

OTHER CLINICAL
FACETS OF
THESE CHILDREN . . .

Girls and boys often have keener insight into what has been going wrong with them than many grownups have believed possible. We have learned how to employ scores of unique rituals and devices to diminish the anxiety that generally accompanies long discouragement, and feelings of grief and failure. Most of us can sidestep these secret feelings enough to avoid much anxiety.

How we do it is not easy to explain, especially to our children. They might not understand. So we rarely let them in on the surprising fact that we *do* remember how it felt to be terribly discouraged and afraid of some great danger or impending destruction. In some situations, this may not have been so bad. Children do need some shielding from utter discouragement, as well as from great danger. They are not rugged enough to stand up to every force in life.

Yet perhaps we frequently underestimate our children in these matters. We sometimes forget that when we were much younger, we still could take what happened without collapsing into dark despair. Many 5-year-olds have guessed why the doctor had to be called in such a hurry, and why his face seemed so serious when he carefully checked a dreadfully painful abdomen. Words are not the only communication link that children swiftly comprehend at such times.

Six and seven-year-olds are not so young that they cannot figure out why their parents become upset by letters from the school that advise repeating grades for some children. I can remember many preschool children who knew their mothers and fathers were afraid of all readiness tests. Ten-year-olds certainly are erudite enough about life to be very much aware of the manifold implications of not getting along well in school.

Report card days are not the only times when most children could tell us quite closely what the chances are of failing or passing. One study I did with a group of fifth-graders I had come to know rather intimately as the psychologist in that school taught me how clearly many children perceive what is happening to them. Only seven out of this group of sixty-two children were not able to *predict* their final marks for the semester in reading, arithmetic, and social science. The boys and girls who were headed for failure knew it, even though they behaved quite stoically about the matter.

Most children, I have come to believe, perceive more of life's realities than we have liked to admit in our own minds. To me, this has meant increasingly that we ought to do far more than we have in the past to enable all children everywhere to meet life *with true dignity,* even when the battle seems to be a losing one.

Discouragement and failure (and death) can be met head-on, with inner strength and dignity. We can teach the children we love and value how to face life in this way. You know parents—and teachers—who are doing it. I can remember many mothers, fathers, and teachers who did it very well, so that their children learned to walk ahead with courage.

The pervading component of the clinical picture of children who are having much difficulty in school is the kind of anxiety that further complicates the trouble. Particularly is this apt to be the case with children who have to meet much perceptual-motor trouble.

The usual reactions of these boys and girls to their difficulties can trigger a mixture of anxiety and irritability in many grownups. For many otherwise intelligent and well-balanced parents and teachers of such children, the *bête noire* in the situation has been the *residue of organicity* that persists even after the emotional aspects have diminished or disappeared. In recent years, many adults have come to believe quite firmly that emotional blocks of some kind are the cause of most children's learning difficulties. To some degree, emotional problems can keep children from doing better in school.

Severe emotional disturbances can make almost any child do very poorly even in a good classroom. All of us have seen such youngsters who needed expert psychotherapy, usually along with other members of the family. Sometimes the teacher needed special help to gain new insights and better techniques for meeting the child in the school atmosphere. Such therapy can bring remarkable improvement in the general mental health of the whole family, thus benefiting the child greatly. I have always been a strong booster for excellent psychotherapy, for it has helped countless children whose school difficulties had much of their origins in subtle brain dysfunction of one kind or another.

I can remember that what troubled many mothers and fathers—and teachers and children too—was the residual organicity that was so slow to respond to any therapy.

"Our child has been on medication so long," said one mother. She was a good mother and had come far in understanding herself as well as her 9-year-old. The old nagging and hot arguments about behaving better had vanished. The child was doing much better in school and at home. But carefully administered tests still revealed jittery reactions, and much the same complex problems of imperception as before. Reading was improving a little, but not as fast as other children advance who have no neurological involvements to bear.

Perhaps because such involvements are so difficult to discern clearly, we tend to minimize them or even say they have little to do with how a child is behaving or learning. One father began to see the truth about his little boy more fully after the man sustained a painful injury to his hand while working in his shop. The tip of one finger had been severed, but the physician was able to suture the piece in place again, and in a few weeks it was almost as good as new. "Only now I can't tell what I am touching with this finger. The doctor says it may be a very long time recovering complete sense of touch again."

The next time this father was in the office, he said he was "beginning to understand what it is like when your nervous system has been injured. The signals from my finger just don't get through. I can't tell what this finger is touching unless I look. It has been a queer sensation . . . . Is this how our Jim has felt, in his own way?"

Any degree of imperception or incoordination leaves a marked communication deficit between the child and the whole world around him. A slight neural injury, imbalance, or dysfunction may leave a youngster quite insecure and anxious about himself and his environment. What one of us would not feel emotionally upset if the signals coming into the brain were even mildly distorted from what other people say are the facts? I have often marveled at the relatively calm and sensible behavior of many children who were constantly facing wide discrepancies in sensation.

Jonathan has been fortunate to live in a family that can take in stride such a hyperactive 10-year-old, and love and value him for what he really is at heart. The boy still shows considerable perceptual difficulty in school. This often has upset him so much that he was quite discouraged and almost unable to try to settle down to learn, no matter how the teacher set the situation. His real name is not Jonathan, but he has liked this name ever since he first came to the office when he was eight. The family physician wanted me to administer some special tests that might give a clearer picture of the boy's school potentials. It did not take long to see that this fine looking lad felt discouraged about himself.

164

"My hands can't do anything right; none of my school papers are neat! Try me, and you'll see I'm not fooling . . . ." So I tried him. He found great difficulty in copying the name *Jonathan* that I printed and then wrote for him at the top of the paper. His performance on many subtests of the Wechsler Intelligence Scale for Children reflected superior intellectual capacity. Yet he was not able to do a good job of copying the algebraic statement I printed for him: $a^2-b^2=(a+b)(a-b)$.

Jonathan had been so jittery in first grade that the parents asked the family physician to help in some way. After examining the child carefully, the physician decided to try special medication at least for a few months. The parents were encouraged to understand their 6-year-old and not expect him to be as tranquil and easygoing as other children. The principal was able to help them too, largely by showing them the good progress Jonathan was making in several ways. The teachers joined in these efforts, with worthwhile results for everyone.

In four years Jonathan has grown wonderfully toward good self-control, as well as in better schoolwork. It would still not be hard to notice some signs of residual organicity at moments when the boy is very tense. But these things no longer are bugaboos to the family or the school. Jonathan is a much happier boy than he used to be.

Children who are fortunate enough (every child deserves to be fortunate enough) to live in an atmosphere where anxiety is kept minimum are more apt to show the kinds of changes Jonathan has made. Low-anxiety children certainly are more apt to want to make good changes in their behavior.

Research on the problem of anxiety in children has been revealing this fact clearly enough for all of us to accept as a working rule for every schoolroom across America. We now know that children grow much better in life situations where anxiety is minimum. In high-anxiety atmosphere, children often *resist* changes for the better.

There are many reasons why children with neurological difficulties behave immaturely at times; why they often are so aggressive and irritable, or seem so anxious. These youngsters are apt to exhibit a broad spectrum of *psychomotor* signs too. The most jittery child still is much more like other children than different from them. His differences are more a matter of degree than of kind.

Some hyperactive children do behave immaturely. Their jitteriness may reflect in many ways, partly depending on the circumstances of the moment. Children such as we are discussing in these chapters may show many of these behaviors and reactions within a few days' span. A particular child may:

——attempt to boss or manipulate the teacher (or parent), sometimes by direct commands, orders, and demands.
——behave very impulsively—indeed, very unpredictably.
——seem very upset; quick to quarrel over trifles.
——talk so much that others weary of trying to listen any longer and are glad when he stops.
——gesture and grimace in the strangest ways and at the oddest moments.
——race from one activity to another, before the first has begun to end or has served much purpose or fun for anyone else.
——seem terrifically rude and impatient, with himself as well as others.
——seem utterly careless about everything; often destructive and hurtful.

These signals generally are related directly to hyperactivity and the concurrent nervousness the child feels but is unable to manage when things have been going badly. The thoughtful teacher usually can understand this, and can take steps to reduce some of the stress the child has been feeling. The situation is rougher to manage in the typical classroom when the child *behaves very immaturely* too, especially when he:

——laughs and giggles at the slightest provocation.
——asks personal questions that can annoy others very much, yet seems unable to realize he is at fault.

—reacts so passively at times that he seems to be asking others to pick on him (as they often do).

— shows many baby traits.

— has less of the quieter reserve that other children his age usually have developed.

Little imagination is needed to see why this hyperactive and somewhat immature child is apt to be very unhappy in some classroom groups and playground situations with other youngsters, or at home with siblings and parents who do not perceive his real problems or want to help him.

Most experienced teachers have seen jittery youngsters whose *aggressive reactions* further complicated the picture. For example, consider the child who:

—suddenly becomes very defensive and hostile, with little apparent cause.

—rarely seems able to admit he has any difficulties or problems.

—just bucks or blocks on tests and recitations.

—often flares into a fight at the drop of a feather.

—often drags out recitations, projects, and plans, until everyone else feels upset at him.

—often exhibits such perfectionism that nothing seems to please him at all.

The child with these behavior tendencies, in addition to the usual pattern of jitteriness, can present a rough problem to the teacher or parent who does not recognize the deeper neurological difficulty and reach for the right medical and psychological help with the youngster. Careful evaluation and diagnosis, followed by the right medication, if necessary, and effective psychological therapy and methods with the child, can change the behavior picture.

Another hyperactive child should be mentioned here because there are so many like him: the hyperactive child with considerable *overlay of anxiety*. In addition to the reflections of inner nervousness that he may show, his anxious feelings are apt to lead him to behave so bizarrely at times that he might seem almost psychotic to someone who did not look carefully at the clinical picture. This child:

— worries excessively much of the time.

— often seems very fearful; may tremble noticeably.

— often shows psychosomatic symptoms including nauseous feelings, headaches, dizziness, and frequent requests to go to the toilet.

— is apt to take wrong meaning from the best intentioned attempts to help him.

— may have such sleep disturbances as night terrors.

— often drifts in daydreams; preoccupation with a toy or a book that enables him to suppress part of the anxious feelings at least for a while.

— may startle easily, and nearly jump out of his seat on a slight noise he had not expected.

Still other hyperactive children show further variations and mixtures of behavior, depending partly on how these girls and boys have been learning to react at home and in school. Day-by-day variations happen with some children, as many parents and teachers could tell you.

Some of these behavior variations might stem from less obvious *electrochemical alterations and imbalances within brain cells* that only recently are being surmised by researchers. There is much to learn about these subtle though potent causes of behavior. Research is just beginning to probe the possibilities.

The alert and thoughtful teacher has the advantage of being openminded about the causes of a child's behavior. Such a teacher can perceive possible neurological and chemical causes beneath plausible psychological causes, in a particular child.

This teacher is better able to understand why the child seems so discouraged about himself at times and why he tries to crash out of the discouragement in ways that so often are more self-defeating than successful.

The chronic undercurrent of discouragement that many of these boys and girls face is a major component of the prob-

168

lem. Imagine how it would feel day after day, year after year, to find yourself improving so slowly in important school skills and subjects—and in general behavior and personality. How long would you go before you felt very discouraged? When your best efforts to *behave better* and *do better in school* still missed the mark, how long would you keep trying? Or would you just give up trying, drift in daydreams, drum on the desk, and disturb the rest of the class?

Would sending such a child to the front office really do much good? It might, if the principal has the wisdom and insight to guess the real problem and refer the boy or girl for careful checking and help. Hyperactive children need to be rightly guessed by alert teachers, before severe discouragement and behavior pathology become part of the picture.

Children do not have to sustain terrible head injuries to incur brain damage. Some infections that invade the central nervous system and brain can disrupt and damage brain areas, leaving a wide range of behavior and learning difficulties. Janet was a case in point.

At seven, in second grade, she was very restless, excitable, and unable to settle down to any kind of work for more than a few minutes. The teacher said Janet upset the class much of the day, and seemed upset herself most of the day, without apparent external cause. The teacher was well aware that Janet had *a problem.*

The child's home life was turmoil too, and the teacher came to the conclusion that the home strife and quarreling were the causes of Janet's bad behavior in school. Certainly the girl seemed confused and conflicted, so the teacher urged referral to a psychologist. Perhaps this would catch up with the parents and help them reach out for the help they needed.

The psychologist was alerted by many signals of organicity in Janet, and recommended a thorough neurological examination. The physician was puzzled by the emotional aspects of the case, and decided to have Janet given an electroencephalogram, to be read and interpreted by the specialist. The diagnosis was *post-encephalitic syndrome* (brain inflamation that had left damage to some functions).

Questioning the parents and the child's previous physicians revealed important facts that had been overlooked. When Janet was four, she had struggled with a severe pneumonia and measles infection, at temperatures hovering around 104 degrees. Some cerebral damage may have occurred at this time. The attending physician had felt the infection had invaded the brain also.

Janet's EEG plainly showed cerebral dysrhythmia—out-of-rhythm and irregular discharge of neuronal cells in the brain. Such abnormal discharge rhythms usually reflect brain malfunction or damage, such as in grand mal.

Janet was really suffering from an *organic* defect that made her particularly sensitive or vulnerable to emotional stress, such as her very discordant home life had been presenting. After the deeper source of trouble was discovered, many parts of the behavior and learning picture that had been overlooked began to be understandable. Janet's old complaints of headaches, dizziness, and increasing discouragement with schoolwork should have been interpreted in light of possible organicity too.

All this does *not* mean that the teacher (or the thoughtful parent, for that matter) must be expected to be a neurologist or psychologist. Yet the alert teacher can learn to recognize such signals as chronic restlessness, tantrums, excitable behavior, dizziness, vomity spells, and excessive fatigue as possible reflections of deeper trouble. These children need to be referred for very careful examination, by specialists extensively experienced in evaluating such youngsters, to rule out organicity before anyone jumps to other diagnostic conclusions.

Knowing that the behavior of a child with signs of cerebral damage or dysfunction probably is *not* something the youngster can *control by himself, with a little effort and determination* will at least keep the teacher flexible in expectations of the child. This teacher is in a happier position to try to discover

170

new ways to encourage such a child to work a little better for short periods, even within the usual classroom group.

All children need to find this earthy kind of wisdom about life and growing things, in teachers as much as in parents. Troubled and anxious children need it too.

When Janet was not quite ten, she came to my office one day between appointments I was keeping in that school. She seemed calm and happy about herself at the moment, so it appeared to be a good time to ask her to help with a study I was making on how clearly children can recognize past feelings of discouragement. She promptly accepted the task, but it took her eight minutes to write these lines about herself. She asked me to let her use my ball-pen to do the job:

How I euse ta fell at school just hat dnd scdred so most of theime and my hand perscdired too

9.3% actual size

Asked to read aloud what she had just written, Janet put on a good front for a moment, then smiled and said, "Maybe I can't do it very well, but I'll try: 'How I used to feel sometimes in school. Just hot and scared and most of the time my hands perspired too.'" Then she added, "I used to wish I could hide when we had to read or write."

Most children are quite aware of their individual differences, particularly in school abilities. Even *academically slow* children can usually tell you where they stand in the class group, and they can feel just as touchy about the matter as brighter children do when they are not getting along well. Hyperactive children, almost by nature, are apt to be sensitive about their school difficulties.

When one 12-year-old was asked how he felt about being promoted to sixth grade even though he had not done nearly that well on the achievement ratings in arithmetic, spelling, reading, and science, he looked a little happier for a brief moment. Then he said, "That will please my father and mother, but it just makes me more scared about next year than I was before. *I* know how dumb I am."

It should never be assumed that every symptom observed in a cerebrally injured child is completely organically caused. In many instances, the child's behavior arises out of his secret but very clear awareness of inner inadequacies and how they limit all hopes and aspirations. Just to tell him that this is life as it comes to most of us does little to regenerate real courage and new hope.

One fine youngster I often remember was quite athetotic (slow, involuntary muscular distortions) much of the time, from central nervous injury at birth. She was a beautiful girl, with toprate parents who valued her warmly. The other children in the class liked her very much. But by fifth grade she secretly felt discouraged about herself. "Look how awful my muscles behave, even when I try so hard to make them steadier. In art class I have trouble copying anything and getting it close to the way I think it should be . . . . Won't I ever be any better; tell me."

Fifth grade was a little late, I thought, to begin to help her feel more hopeful and encouraged about herself. First grade would have been a better time to tackle the real problem. The third-grade teacher noted the child's perceptual-motor-language difficulties, commenting on the permanent record form, "She has trouble in copying anything, and she is often very nervous. Poorly coordinated in most games. The child should be seen by the psychologist if these difficulties do not clear up next year." No referral was made the next year. "She is such a nice child when she feels calm, it would be a shame to suspect there really is anything wrong with her that would require a psychologist to check," the teacher had said.

172

Children do not largely inherit personality and behavior traits. These are mostly learned within the home, at school, out in the neighborhood, and in countless human contacts.

Perhaps by nature, girls are inclined to be more submissive than boys, and more influenced by what they believe adults expect of them. Boys are a little more apt to behave aggressively than girls. (These broad differences are supported by many studies, such as those made by May, Terman, Jones, Tudor-Hart, and others.) The same degree of lack of socialization in boys and in girls is likely to manifest itself in more serious aggressive forms among the boys, other factors being equal between the groups. Boys are more apt to get into greater difficulty via aggressive behavior and reactions than girls are, in the same circumstances. Many more boys than girls are likely to have to warm the front office chairs in the usual school. Girls probably have just as many obstreperous impulses as boys have, but girls seem to follow through fewer times, and in less aggravating ways.

Couple all this with the findings of many studies on brain injury among children that show injury to boys much higher than to girls, and the boy-girl ratios in clinic referral statistics seem to be in line with the general psycho-neurological data.

Teachers who have studied modern psychology *and its neurological foundations* are not surprised to read that careful researches on children who sustained brain injury show a far greater proportion of neurotic behavior traits than other children do. These children could be expected to behave more irritably many times, with less self-control in frustrating situations. Sometimes the lack of self-control may be taken as nonchalance by a teacher or parent who is not bothered by rashness in the child. Children with diffuse injury from encephalitis often show such signs mixed in with the usual clinical picture of hyperactivity and imperception difficulties.

One father said he had "tried just about everything" to help his boy behave and learn better in school. The mother probably had overguarded the boy in some ways, especially since he had nearly died at birth from lack of oxygen during a long labor. The father often took the boy on fishing and camping trips, and there was a marvelously warm rapport between them as a good son who loved a good father. "But he still doesn't do well in school, though the teacher told us he is not a slow child in potential. . . . What have we left undone?"

Such parents need—and surely deserve—the very best encouragement and support. They become secretly discouraged too, and their feelings of secret despair are sometimes more difficult to help in the right ways than whatever may be the child's basic trouble. This much I have learned out of my own experience as the psychologist in several school systems and clinics, where many parents asked the question, "Tell me, where have we failed. Is it too late to undo the harm?"

Bad parents have never asked me such a question. Good parents have. This fact greatly affected whatever answers I could have offered, unless I felt I could honestly begin by saying, "You are trying to be a good parent. There are many things about your child to show that this is so. In your place, I might have done differently, yet perhaps no better. Let's put our heads together now and see what can be done to help your child a little more. We will have some success, I am confident."

Twenty years ago, I might have used a more analytical approach with such a parent, just letting the father or mother wander uselessly in thoughts about what should have been done. The experience of intervening years has taught me to avoid such moody conversation with parents, whether they seem to have done the best they can or not. Who could really judge anyway? And what good would such judging do to help a child now? Probably very little.

As some children add birthdays, they gradually learn to manage *and divert* earlier hyperactive behavior. But simply growing older does not always clear these troubles, as many adolescents and young adults could testify.

Keener clinical perceptiveness on the part of more physicians and psychologists in the last decade has been focusing better attention on possible organic foundations of behavior and personality disturbances in older children. Descriptions such as *sociopath* are less used now than a decade ago.

Some of these changes in diagnostic attitudes have been paralleling the advent of many new psychological instruments that are proving to have reliable discriminating power in the hands of skilled and knowledgeable clinicians. Able physician-psychologist teams are now able to spot the real sources of trouble in many boys and girls who used to be tabbed simply as character disorders or pathologic behavior cases that had to act-out in peculiar ways.

Of course by adolescent years such a boy or girl who has faced a long span of discouragement, particularly in school, often presents a complicated behavior mixture involving emotional maladjustment. In many instances this development would be quite predictable and expected. Camilla Anderson and H. H. Plymate, physicians at Salem State Hospital, in Oregon, have extensively elaborated this point in their paper on "Management of the Brain-Damaged Adolescent" in the *American Journal of Orthopsychiatry*, April, 1962. The senior author of the team, Camilla Anderson, has for many years been studying organic factors predisposing children and adolescents to schizophrenic breakdown. She prefers the more definitive term *association deficit pathology* (ADP) with most of the children generally thought of as possibly brain-injured, because they exhibit much of the Strauss syndrome.

Whatever the designation we prefer, there is wide agreement now among top level researchers—Lauretta Bender, Charles Bradley, Edgar Doll, Alfred Strauss, Laura Lehtinen, Sol Levy, Camilla Anderson, and a score of others—on the signs of such trouble in children and young adults.

Equally wide agreement is swiftly coming among top professional workers that the major symptom of abnormal behavior in so many difficult adolescents probably rises out of subtle neurologic defect of some kind, perhaps incurred early in life. Also, that in most instances the disturbance is present irrespective of interpersonal or environmental factors. The next ten years of intensive work on the problem may give us answers to some important questions about ADP, especially whether the chief cause has been cerebral anoxia or some such neurophysical injury, as so many researchers have believed for a long time.

A high percentage of adolescents and young adults who seem to belong within this ADP catagory have histories revealing longstanding signs including these:

— general feelings of restlessness, with little regard to the mildness or lack of pressure in the surrounding life situation.

— low threshhold to distraction, along with lowered tolerance to the usual frustrations that are apt to crop up in living.

— extraordinary preoccupation with some specific activity, even when this activity seems to return so little real satisfaction.

— unusual lack of normal fears in some instances, coupled at times with a parallel lack of normal warmth and sympathy for others who are in rough spots in life.

— often obvious motor incoordination, plus, in many cases, poor comprehension and control of physical power.

— marked incapacity to handle abstract conceptual problems, sometimes reflected by poor sense of humor and seeming inability to *catch on* to things.

— frequent discipline problems, often nearly chronic defiance even of good help from good sources.

— frequently increasing scholastic difficulty hardly in line with what carefully administered tests of capacity would predict.

— wide range of multiple physical inadequacies, particularly of the digestive system.

— high tendency to be anxious, bursting into tempery displays, behaving *neurotically* about anything that is not working out as expected.

176

Essentially the same characteristics would describe many younger children who reflect association deficit pathology. The list would also fit most children with known cerebral injuries. Emotional upsets can overlay and complicate these clinical pictures, of course, but many good teachers I have known were able to recognize the mixture and understand its dynamics well enough to meet classroom situations wisely. Most ADP children are apt to seem rather:

——shallow in ideation and imagination and out of line with what carefully administered tests of intellectual capacities would infer.

——easily tumbled into anxiety or panic in situations that demand much change or adaptation—again, out of line with expected behavior.

The high correlations between the clinical ratings of such children and adolescents who show signs of ADP and the incidence of abnormalities in their electroencephalograms is interesting and pertinent. Camilla Anderson notes that in several studies of children with behavior disorders the correlations were so high that the information was nearly discarded for that very reason! The preconception that behavior disorders are psychodynamic in origin, and not organic, has been strongly held in many quarters, even to the point where clear EEG data have been thought invalid if not inconsequential. This should not surprise thoughtful teachers who have lived awhile in the world where widely held opinion can overrule new facts.

Fortunately the central nervous system is designed to be sturdy enough to match the usual stresses in a child's life. At least we like to believe that this is true, and in so hoping, we subtly say no to the idea that the brain and its nerve systems are by no means indestructible, particularly in childhood years with their high incidence of head injuries, severe illnesses, and other dangers.

True enough, the same behavior and school difficulties in

several children can have varying etiologies—head injuries, encephalitis, vascular disease, neoplastic disease, and damage from toxins, for example. Such multiplicity of possible cause has tempted many parents and teachers to reach for more *hopeful* psychodynamic diagnoses. This is really not so hard to understand, in such cases, for children do seem quite indestructible. How else do most of them ever survive what happens to them!

The universe of intricate electrochemical organization that comprises a single neuron anywhere in the body's vast nervous system is still beyond the resolving power of the finest microscope. There may never be lenses that will make these submolecular organizations visible to the eye. But the modern electroencephalograph and analyzer are bringing some phases of these minute universes into another kind of view for us, without opening the skull or hurting the patient in any way.

Electroencephalography has some problems of its own, however, that must be borne in mind to avoid thinking of it as the perfect tool. What present instruments can do, they do excellently: accurately amplifying and recording the wave form, voltage, and frequency of some of the currents arising in and activating certain cortical areas of the living brain. The physical nature of the human brain brings only approximately one-third of the total cortical area within the measurement capacity of the EEG. Currents from other cortical areas deep in brain folds and fissures are at present definitely believed to exist, though without much direct proof. Currents in such structures as the thalamus and other *inner* brain areas may have to wait a long time for far more sensitive recording techniques to be devised before their electrical nature can be perceived. Some structural defects in the brain do not reflect in definite EEG abnormalities, as now recorded.

Out of extensive research several facts are increasingly clear. All brain and other nervous system functions are now believed to be electrochemical at base. This concept has been altering much of the thinking about why we behave as we do, and particularly why organic changes in the systems of the body have *psychologic* effects. These advances in knowledge and understanding of ourselves have not always been easily won.

Research findings are not always clear-cut or sharply definitive. The experience and wisdom of the scientist-researcher are still needed to *interpret* the data to reveal truth, mixed with as little of the chaff of pseudo-truth as possible.

The electroencephalograph—at least in its present stage of development and use—does not reflect all kinds and levels of brain function or dysfunction. Cerebral disorder and dysfunction can exist without severely disrupting a child's behavior, and without clear evidence in the EEG. Many instances of children with known brain injury have shown this to be true.

As much as we might like to believe that an apparently normal EEG definitely means that the brain is functioning completely normally, this hope is not attainable at present. Exacting studies, however, are throwing brighter light on these problems year by year.

Leo Hanvik in March, 1961 reported his study of cerebral dysfunction in children, in the *American Journal of the Diseases of Children:* Children coming to guidance clinic were routinely given EEGs as part of the examination procedure. These children were quite typical of those children referred for such evaluation and diagnosis, including the usual range of *behavior* and *learning* difficulties. Of 148 consecutive EEGs, Hanvik found thirty-seven per cent were plainly abnormal and reflected brain damage.

Marquardson and Harvald, of Frederiksberg Hospital, Copenhagen, Denmark, have reported an enlightening study in the Scandanavian journal, *Acta Neurologica,* 1964. Correlations were studied between EEG and autopsy findings in twenty cases of acute vascular lesions of the cerebrum or cerebellum. Two patients with extensive damage to the pons area, deep within the brain, had shown normal EEG during the state of coma. The upper brain stem will provoke slow-wave abnormalities in the EEG, *probably owing to damage to cephalic portions of the reticular activating system.*

On the other hand, Marquardson and Harvald found, even extensive damage to the pons or cerebellar areas of the brain may not appreciably show in the EEG. This fact keeps wise physicians and neurologists cautious about ruling out possible brain dysfunction in a child simply because the EEG seems to be within normal range. As engineer-scientists improve and refine the instruments, this difficulty probably will be remedied at least to some degree.

Yet even with present EEG techniques, remarkable progress has come in the last decade in understanding something of the *subcellular electrochemical activity* particularly in the systems of the living brain that we recognize indirectly when we use such words as thinking, feeling, doing, remembering, hearing, seeing, composing, hoping, and even believing.

These complex brain activities do not have to be absolutely perfect in function for a child to be happy, well behaved, self-activating, and self-actualizing in wholesome ways. On the other hand, slight disturbances anywhere in the intricate electrochemical networks may disrupt a child and make him behave badly in some situations.

Studies in recent years in such centers as Duke University have been throwing light on the electrochemical *cycles* that govern much of our lives. There is mounting evidence that every person has an in-built *time table* or cycle of energy that can be recognized if we notice the signals. Everyone has at times felt *more productive, calmer, better integrated, and able to think* than on other days. Children show these cycles of greater and lesser potentiality too. Someday perhaps not far ahead, we will gear school and learning situations more wisely than we do now, to each child's *inner* schedule of effectiveness, and not to an arbitrary outside clock or calendar.

Several excellently designed studies have been reported within the last few years comparing the performance of nonbrain-injured preschool children with that of preschool youngsters known to have suffered cerebral damage. One study reported in *Psychological Monographs,* Volume 77, Number 11, for 1963 is pertinent to our discussion in this chapter. The members of the research team are all notable in the field of psychology, and worked in collaboration with able neurologists. The team included Claire Ernhart, Frances Graham, Peter Eichman, Joan Marshall, and Don Thurston, who carried out part two of the study.

All of the seventy brain-injured children were found to be significantly, though not equally, impaired in the performance functions that were measured. *These children were less impaired in personality functioning than in other aspects of their lives.* This is worth noting here again, for it parallels what every thoughtful teacher can remember parents saying in some conferences: "It is so hard to understand why my child can behave so sensibly around the house most of the time and still be doing so poorly in schoolwork. I can't believe there can be much wrong in that brain. . . ."

The recent study by Tueber and Rudel, reported in *Developmental Medicine: Child Neurology* (1962, Vol. 4), is especially significant in illustrating the complex relationship between development and the effects of brain injury in children. Age-when-injured was held close to constant by studying children who sustained injury at or near birth. Age-of-testing was the variable, ranging from five to eighteen years of age. In this study, performance of noninjured children and brain-injured children changed systematically with age, but differently for different functions, depending quite clearly on the pathological course of development in the injured children.

Many of the brain-injured children that Tueber and Rudel studied were not very jittery or hyperkinetic. The degree of jitteriness in a particular youngster sometimes does not seem to correspond very closely with the rest of the syndrome. Trying to screen out all the children who might be brain-injured by noting only whether they are hyperkinetic would still miss a large percentage of the cases.

There is abundant evidence now from careful studies that abnormal electrical activity in the human brain (including such activity that an EEG may reveal) tends to be much higher in children from three to twelve, and then later on in aging persons seventy and beyond, than in other age ranges. Many aging brains produce electroencephalographic patterns quite similar to those of young children.

The behavioral implications of this are not yet fully understood. How much the EEG findings imply *second childhood* is an interesting matter for conjecture if not further research. Neurologists now are certain that whatever derangements bring, electrical abnormalities *are molecular and chemical in nature*. Their histologic correlates are beginning to be surmised in some instances.

The complex structure and electron pattern of ribonucleic acid (RNA) may yet prove to hold some of the answers to the questions of how and why the brain can remember. RNA still is so expensive and in such short supply that there have not been enough experiments with it for biochemists to be certain about its functions in the brain and its nervous systems. Some studies, however, have indicated marvelous potentials for RNA when more is known about it.

Donald E. Cameron, reknowned neuropsychiatrist and professor on the faculty of McGill University, in Montreal, has found that giving RNA to aging persons markedly improved their ability to remember accurately. Several studies with animals have shown that RNA increases *in the brain* when working at learning tasks. Exactly how RNA functions in the brain cells and nerve fibers to bring about better learning power is not fully understood at present, but we do know it always happens, in both animal and human brains.

Some of the studies have been so dramatic that they would never have been believed even in scientific circles a century ago. Allen Jacobson, of the University of California at Los Angeles, educated rats to search for food when they heard a certain clicking sound. Brain cells from these rats were injected into *untaught* rats that had not learned to seek food when they heard the clicking sound. But now these animals behaved as though they had previously learned what to do about the sound.

Do brain cells carry a special kind of *intelligent learning and memory* along with them, even when injected into another brain? Apparently they do. And perhaps the secret of the transfer of intelligence is tied up somewhere in the function of RNA, along with the subcellular electrochemical changes now believed to take place in many parts of the brain when we are thinking and learning.

Whatever the answer to this question about ourselves and our potentials, we are coming closer to the full truth. Even these new glimpses of what we can do some fair day, perhaps not far ahead, are thrilling.

All these guesses and discoveries are at least good beginnings, for they portend hope for many children. The next twenty-five years may see the development and application of electronic instruments to the diagnosis of subtle neurologic dysfunction that will outshine all of the advances thus far.

Children with dyslexia (reading disability) have been coming under more exacting neurologic study recently, through the aid of new electroencephalographic techniques. The findings have been adding scientific weight to earlier researches into possible organicity in many of these children. It now is thought that dyslexia is not *commonly* caused by slight head injuries or *ordinary* infections alone. Kinds of central nervous system impairment that correlate highly with EEG abnormality do not always bring marked reading disability unless complicated by some mixture of intellectual deficit (associational, usually), perceptual-motor defects, and/or epilepsy.

Any of these possible complications is apt to be the clinical picture of a child with much difficulty in learning to read and manage symbolic material. Part of the deeper organic cause may be somewhere in the thalamus, where synthesis and comprehension probably take place. This is now generally believed to be the case. Research neurologists feel it explains why some brain-injured children have such extensive *imperception* problems.

Thalamic dysfunction may also be a large factor in the aphasic behavior of many children with other signals of brain disorder or injury. There is a wide overlap in the behavior and learning characteristics of such children and others who can be classified as having perceptual-motor-language difficulties.

How well a child with such difficulties may progress in good learning conditions depends on several factors, some of them supporting, others limiting. The prognosis in any case still is partly an *educated guess*. From this point of view, the teacher need not be afraid to work along with the psychologist who knows the child clinically.

Prognosis of a child's *language* progress correlates closely with the level or degree of the perceptual-motor difficulty. Several levels can be differentiated sufficiently here for the teacher to estimate a child's likely progress in language, reading, and arithmetic—symbolic areas of behavior:

Very slight perceptual-motor immaturity in a child usually reflects simply an overall delay in development. Especially if positive changes are beginning to be apparent in this child's speech and language, as other indices of intelligence are increasing, the prognosis is usually *good*. This child may do quite well in the regular school, with extra help if necessary in a good special class group for such boys and girls.

Moderate perceptual-motor distortion that stems mostly from peripheral disability in the child (and thus can be largely compensated by surgery, prosthetic aids or appropriate therapeutic techniques) generally permits a *guarded-to-good* prognosis. Special glasses, large type books, hearing aids, and corrective therapy, sometimes in special classes, can bring great changes in these children.

184

The right caution always is in order whenever a child is being described as probably cerebrally damaged in some way. The best correlations obtained thus far between *signals* of possible brain dysfunction in children and demonstrable damage in these youngsters is not so high that other causes of at least part of the difficulty in a particular child can be ruled out without careful checking. Best reliability of diagnosis comes when the family physician, neurologist, endocrinologist, psychiatrist, psychologist, teacher, counselor, and parent sit down together to look at every aspect of the child's behavior and case history. The *tentative diagnosis* coming out of this team approach is likely to be much closer to the truth than the best thinking of any one of the team could produce alone.

One troubled boy I remember had such a normal appearing EEG for the first ten minutes of the record that the physician-electroencephalographer wondered why the youngster had been referred. The boy's record in the next few minutes began to reflect a cortex that could be quite irritable at times. The second EEG, about two months later, showed clearer signals of possible cortical trouble, although this second record still was not diagnostically conclusive. This lack of absolute diagnostic clarity in many children's cases should not be discouraging for anyone who has considered the magnificent complexity of the human brain and nervous system, plus all the other organ-systems of the body. That any such highly interrelating systems are even vaguely understandable is in itself nearly beyond expectation.

The major life purposes of a child's intricate central nervous system are not simply to make an electronic machine draw wiggly lines on a moving sheet of paper, or to differentiate geometric figures from a background, or even to duplicate words and phrases that may make little sense to the child at the moment.

Yet, *with the right wisdom, and training, and experience,* the physician, neurologist, psychiatrist, psychologist, and teacher too, can see in a child's attempts to do such things some signals that could reflect deeper defects or dysfunction. We need never feel embarrassed that the signals many times are *soft* enough to make us cautious in interpreting them. Such caution is part of the essence of all wisdom. This kind of intelligent caution has gradually been altering our point of view about boys and girls who used to be labeled as "retarded" simply because they did not respond as well as other children in some situations.

Many children once thought to be autistic—very withdrawn and self-centered—are now being viewed in the new and clearer light of the complex neurology and electrochemistry of the brain and nervous system. Such children often show marked time lags between afferent (incoming) auditory nerve impulses and efferent (comprehending and outgoing) reactions. In some of these children, several seconds may elapse before the child can respond to the very simple command he has just *heard*. To the child, this delay can be chaotic and comparable to trying to watch a movie where the sound is out of synchronism with the picture. The chronic confusion gradually forces some children who have this cerebral problem to withdraw and not even try to hear or talk anymore. At the moment, this kind of defense behavior resolves some of the secret problems the child has been finding so hard to bear.

These boys and girls need wise and thoughtful teachers who at least are alert to some of the learning problems that even subtle brain dysfunction can bring. Teachers with warm and practical hope, a growing knowledge of methods and materials that might help with such children, *and an easygoing kind of inventiveness* on the spur of the moment in the classroom, are still the major, most important ingredients in any programs to help these children.

Such a teacher —knowledgeable about jittery children and ready to work in close cooperation with the physician and psychologist—can turn many children who used to feel secretly but utterly discouraged into *new* children with remarkable *new* desire to learn.

Teachers who like to work with boys and girls who have learning difficulties often consider such changes in their children as "ordinary occurrences." They know that:

——*moderate perceptual-motor disturbances* that reflect possible central sensory impairment still permit a prognosis of *guarded to good.* These children mostly need expert examination and prescription, just as all the others, by a multidiscipline team, to prevent overlooking critical facets of the clinical picture. Such disturbances usually rise out of fluctuations in the reception of stimuli that in turn produce fluctuations in the child's organization powers, and then in his responses to what he has perceived at the integrative level.

——*more severe perceptual-motor disturbance* in a child may be somewhat less hopeful, with a *poorer* prognosis in some cases. The greater the child's general retardation, the poorer the prognosis may be. Yet these children too, can benefit wonderfully in very well taught special classes, where the teacher looks on every child with a practical kind of hope and ingenuity.

No child exactly *fits* any catagory day by day, and hardly year after year. Every child deserves to be seen in a bright new light every morning. Good teachers are more interested in a youngster's *signs of progress* than what catagory he was in a few weeks ago.

Maurice Laufer, physician and director of Emma Pendleton Bradley Hospital, in Riverside, Rhode Island, has pointed out again what Paul Schilder used to urge young interns at Bellevue Hospital to keep in mind: Abnormal functioning of the central nervous system does not always rise out of a structural injury or defect that must happen first. *Abnormal functioning may come out of an abnormal process that has been going on a long time.* Idiopathic epilepsy, seen in so many children, is a pertinent example of this two-way interaction possible within any of us. These children sometimes show epileptic symptoms so clearly that it is difficult to believe the examining physician when he says he can discern practically none of the neurophysical picture he would expect to find.

Children who have felt very discouraged and very defeated long enough have been known to develop many kinds of organic troubles that have added to the original problem. Just which part of the ensuing mixture of problems could then be labeled as cause or result might be hard to know. The delineation becomes misty and less definable with passing years.

A swift quarter-century ago, Paul Schilder was insisting that the relationship between organicity and emotional disturbance can be a two-way street, one leading eventually to the other. Research across the intervening decades has been supporting his conjecture more and more.

Part of the answer to all this is for schools to go all out to help every child gain the best mental health possible. Good teachers do not feel apologetic about such concern for a child's health and progress. All aspects of a child's life—physical, social, intellectual, and spiritual—have rightful places in this total concern, for they are not separate phases or entities within the child. Each is a facet of the whole youngster; each is vital to his integrity.

Whatever enables the child to regain the right self-esteem and hope about himself is worth accomplishing as early as possible for the child.

12

SOME PHARMACOTHERAPY AIDS ARE HERE NOW . . .

Biochemists in scores of pharmaceutical laboratories are hard at work discovering and building new drugs that are very effective in helping children who are jittery and easily upset. Some of the drugs recently discovered are especially effective with children who have been quite anxious, depressed, and discouraged about themselves because of marked perceptual-motor-communication difficulties.

Newer drugs now available are more powerful than some of the earlier ones were, yet the new ones are safer and less toxic in many cases. We are on the threshold of an unprecedented era in psychopharmacology, with master chemists leading the field. Many jittery children who would have been thought beyond much real salvaging from central nervous system troubles a few years ago are now being helped to behave amazingly well, in school and at home.

The next decade will undoubtedly bring even greater advances in good drug therapy with these boys and girls. Physicians and pharmacists even now must study to keep abreast of the increasing literature on new drugs for these purposes. Practical pharmaceutic help is coming in many neurologic disorders that used to be labeled in such gloomy terms as degenerative or heredodegenerative—the once thought *inescapable* effects of aging and hereditary factors. Biochemists are beginning to find ways to pierce these ancient barriers to better health.

Recent discoveries, for example, are pointing to long-hoped-for breakthroughs in ways to entice vital enzymes in the body to alter and *adjust* slightly, to produce interorgan-system health and harmony of function where chronic ailments and malfunctions used to be accepted as the best we could expect in life. Within the last year, radical discoveries have occurred regarding the multifaceted functions of hormones—particularly the sex-controlling hormones—that may enable us to slow down some of the *aging* processes in some organs, including the brain and nerve system networks.

These new drugs add greatly to the physician's effective tools and techniques, giving him marvelous new power to help where little help of any kind used to be available. It is thrilling to see what such a drug as Mellaril did to help a child who had been so jittery that no school wanted the boy. Now he is doing moderately well in a good special class for children with such problems. The new era holds great promise for these youngsters.

Yet the discovery and production of such pharmacotherapeutic aids is not free from dangers. Physicians are looking for effective drugs, and are studying hard to be able to use these drugs for best results with children as well as grownups.

Having powerful drugs at hand, and knowing how to sidestep the inherent dangers in using these agents, are two widely different matters, as any physician could tell us out of his own experience. A drug potent enough to alter subcellular functions and balances can be powerful enough to alter in wider ways, even to damage permanently.

This has been joltingly true in many cases. Some drugs that seemed quite safe when they were being used in the laboratory stage, before marketing, have still shown lethal potential in a particular child, with side-effects that took quick recognition by the physician to manage.

For these reasons, thoughtful physicians have been rightly cautious in using some drugs with some children. The physician's intensive and extensive training and experience qualifies him as the authority in any matter of what drug a child should be given. This is no light responsibility in cases where the prescribed drug may be dangerous as well as necessary.

The school physician is the key member of the team whenever medication is involved with any child. He should make all such decisions. Other team members—the school nurse, psychologist, teacher, counsellor, and parent—must work together with the physician, of course, for maximum effectiveness. In such a team setting, I can remember many children who were remarkably helped by the right medication at the right time.

Clinical and experimental psychology have long had major interests in neuropsychiatric research, particularly with children who may have suffered brain injury. Psychologists have developed many techniques for discerning subtle perceptual-motor dysfunctions, in young children as well as in adults. These instruments are gaining increasing acceptance in neurology, as well as in education, with good results for children in both areas. This rising tide of interest was spurred greatly just before 1950, when such researchers as Mayer-Gross and Walker were publishing their studies on the effect of intravenous injection of glutamic acid on the return of consciousness in children who had been in hypoglycemic coma (coma from severe drop in blood sugar). The glutamic acid injections markedly accelerated return to consciousness in most instances.

One very discouraged 13-year-old I remember gradually drifted into a slump in school: Poorer marks, lassitude, and moodiness that had the teacher wondering whether the girl was heading for some kind of psychotic breakdown. The counsellor recognized more of the physical signals, and called the school physician to help. Examination soon made diagnosis possible—hypoglycemia, with depression. The youngster admitted she had ". . . just quit eating, I felt so discouraged. . . ." Her mother had told the girl that she should either bring home better marks or quit school and go to work to earn the food she ate and the clothes she wore. The youngster had been headed for serious difficulty, perhaps some degree of hypoglycemic trouble, but the teacher noticed and did something more than scold her for behaving so peculiarly. The physician's diagnostic skill and help changed the picture toward good health again.

In hepatic coma, a disorder reflecting deeper disturbances in the metabolisms of oxydation, sodium glutamate has been found to aid and speed the clearing of consciousness. The biochemical processes involved are not yet completely understood in such recoveries, and the action of glutamic acid on brain metabolism seems to be even more complex, so that theories about it are quite controversial too.

Paralleling extensive research on many new tranquilizing compounds and cerebral stimulants, great efforts have been invested in studies of psychoses-inducing and psychoses-reducing drugs. These investigations have brought to light valuable knowledge about many of the biochemical conditions preceding and accompanying psychotic illnesses and recovery from these difficulties.

These studies permit some general conclusions about major groups of psychotherapeutic drugs now coming into common use with children who are very jittery and reflect attention difficulties especially in the classroom.

Improvement in emotional stability and general behavior occurs more often than any radical change in intellectual ability, in children being given the proper drugs. Behavior improvement in some cases has been so remarkable that the child's entire school picture has changed, sometimes in a few weeks or months. These children often seem to do so much better on tests that teachers may believe great changes have happened in intellectual potentials. The simple truth may just lie in the child's improvement in ability to attend to the tasks

192

One 11-year-old improved so much from November to June that the teacher could hardly believe the psychologist had not used "some kind of magic therapy" on the boy. The only therapy had been the family physician's prescription of one of the special drugs now available to help jittery children be a little calmer and milder in behavior. In October the boy had been so stormy in the classroom that no day passed without some blow-up. His spelling was very poor, though he *read* nearly up to grade level. The teacher said she "was exhausted" with him sometimes by lunch period. At home, his mother said, the boy was often terrifically touchy and explosive over the least difficulty. She gladly asked the physician to help in any way possible.

These designs the boy drew from memory after short exposure, before medication had been started and later in June, reflect something of the great change in the boy's personality as well as his schoolwork across the interval. His spelling marks came from failing level to C in the same time:

Before medication   With medication

65% actual size

By June, there still were subtle signs of motor and perceptual difficulty at times, but his general behavior and health picture had cleared remarkably. His blood pressure had become normal, he rested better at night, and he was a much happier boy all around, at school as well as at home.

to be accomplished, employing the intellect he always possessed but used to be nearly unable to utilize because he was so jittery and anxious.

Behavior changes that do occur are generally more in terms of degree than of kind. The child's behavior under drugs is more apt to be mildly modified than completely altered. He still does the things he used to do, but he is better able to manage his behavior and not be so difficult to control or teach. He seems less intensive, less impulsive, a little more open, and ready to be helped. These are small changes in some ways, but they have great effects on the total picture of his behavior in the classroom as well as around the neighborhood. One 12-year-old said, "Inside I sometimes feel just as jittery as before, but now I can turn down the feeling a little and not behave like I used to do. I'm happier about myself now too; I don't get as discouraged as I used to feel. . . ."

The right psychotherapeutic drugs apparently enable the child to govern his emotions better, so that the old extremes of feelings and behavior are less often exhibited and he behaves more normally. Even this modification is wonderful in some children, as many teachers and parents could tell you.

Some children show greater improvement in schoolwork than others, of course, even with the same drugs. These differences should not surprise thoughtful teachers or parents who keep in mind the wide variations possible in the nature and extent of the neurological circumstances in different youngsters.

Any drugs capable of marked psychotherapeutic action should, of course, be employed with caution, under the supervision and control of the physician who has known the child awhile and can prescribe wisely in the case. The safest drugs may still have peculiar side effects in some instances. The experienced physician is best able to estimate the proper dosage of a drug in a particular case, to bring desired changes in the child's behavior and feelings. This is why all drugs and compounds for psychotherapeutic purposes have been restricted to prescription by the attending physician, and are not available otherwise.

No thoughtful person would oppose these safeguards. Wonderful as many of the new drugs now seem, none of them are completely free from possible danger in some situations. What drug should be utilized in a particular case, what the dosage should be, and what effects should be regarded as possible danger signals, is the professional province of the trained physician who knows the child and can intelligently weigh the risks that may be involved.

The neuropsychiatrist who has had extensive training and experience with children is often in the best position to direct the use of drugs for psychotherapeutic purposes. Many physicians prefer to refer children needing this help to such a specialist. In turn, the specialist may ask the parent, teacher, school nurse, and psychologist to help to watch the child closely for any changes in behavior that should guide any increase or reduction in the prescription. The primary responsibility for choice of drug and prescription for its use in any case, however, must be with the physician in charge of the child.

The school physician, school nurse, and psychologist share responsibility for keeping the teacher alert and knowledgeable about the effects of a particular drug on the child's reactions and behavior. Good teachers like to be part of the therapeutic team in this respect, and are open to the right kind of instruction to do their part well.

The drugs briefly listed in this chapter comprise only a few of the many now available from pharmaceutical houses for medical use with children who are jittery and have much school trouble because of various neurological disturbances. The list is offered simply to introduce interested teachers to this newly adapted field of biochemical aids with such children. Every jittery youngster might not benefit equally by administration of such drugs, but many children have been helped to gain a toehold on better behavior with such drugs. This behavioral improvement in turn has enabled these boys and girls to get along at least with a little less anxiety and frustration in school. Parents and teachers often have reported happy changes in children who were taking the proper drugs to help them feel calmer and less depressed about themselves.

Toxicity and peculiar side-effects are always inherent dangers with any drug powerful enough to alter any of the central nervous system functions. For this reason any child who may need such pharmacotherapeutic help should be under the care of a physician who will take all the time necessary to keep careful watch for signals of trouble. This caution must be wisely enforced by all the persons who are helping the child with his difficulty. No one but the prescribing physician should make any changes of any kind in the medication. With this caution strictly adhered to by everyone, many drugs now are being safely employed to help such children as we are discussing in this book.

Dilantin (diphenylhydantoin) and *Mesantoin* (methylphenylethylhydantoin) are examples of some of the drugs that may be used by the physician to alter the clinical picture of epilepsy in children. When carefully prescribed and supervised for possible side-effects, these drugs have enabled many children to live freer of the old stormy behavior patterns. These children begin to take courage again, and go forward with less fear about themselves. In many children I can remember, the changes in general behavior and attitude were remarkable. Helen, an attractive fifth-grader, said she used to wish she could run far away "where nobody would know or care who I was or what I did. . . . Now I never feel that way any more. . . . I'm looking forward to being in junior high with the rest of my friends. . . ."

Before the development of anticonvulsants such as Dilantin and Mesantoin, epileptic children had to suffer their disorders as best they could. The clinical picture sometimes was a very gloomy and discouraging one for the parents as well as the child. These drugs have been proving very effective with children who show a wide range of behavior disturbances often associated with the kinds of electroencephalographic patterns seen in clearly epileptic children. Physicians sometimes prescribe these anticonvulsants in alternation with such a drug as phenobarbital, with added effectiveness with certain children. Here is where the physician's full and specialized knowledge as an internist and neurologist can be of great value to the young patient.

Librium (chlordiazepoxide hydrochloride) has been the first of a new class of psychotherapeutic agents developed for safer and better management of common emotional distrubances in children as well as in adults. The drug is unrelated chemically — and clinically — to other tranquilizing and antidepressant compounds now in use with upset children. Librium appears to be one of the safest and most effective drugs available in treating children who are very jittery and anxious. It has been used very successfully with children who are fearful and tense or compulsive in behavior.

School troubles stemming from such deeper causes often abate so remarkably with the administration of Librium that teachers and parents are surprised by the change in the child in a few days. One teacher said of a third-grader, "He behaves so much better now that I can hardly believe he was so hard to manage two weeks ago. The other children have noticed the change too."

Children who used to behave quite obsessively and compulsively have been helped remarkably by the drug in many instances. Skeletal muscle spasticity, such as those resulting from injuries to the spinal cord or brain areas, respond well to Librium. Children with poor muscle tone or athetosis (repeated involuntary muscle distortions, usually from brain injury) are often greatly helped by the drug. When the dosage has not been large, the drug can be stopped without withdrawal symptoms. This factor has given the drug wide use by physicians in many kinds of jittery patterns in children.

Equanil and *Miltown* (meprobamate) have been used with

good results with many children who are convulsive at times, perhaps with anxiety and muscle tension. These drugs permit calmer rest and sleep, partly by relaxing muscles and reducing anxiety. With high dosages, meprobamate compounds may tend toward chronic dependency on the drug. In the usual dosage range with children, however, this hazard is slight, particularly when the child is in the care of a wise physician who knows how to employ minimal dosage for adequate results.

Meprospan is just a new dosage form that has been designed to release meprobamate slowly over a period of time. This is advantageous with children who are busy in school all day, with no chance to go to the nurse's office for medication at prescribed intervals. No doubt, the next year or two will see many drugs come out in this new slow-release design, for just such uses.

Benadryl (diphenhydramine hydrochloride) has been helpful with some children who show primary behavior disorders involving much anxiety and flighty reactions, as is so often part of the clinical picture in brain damage. These children need such support to feel a little calmer, less easily frightened and upset, and less discouraged about themselves. In many cases, these children begin to rest better at night, with fewer night terrors and bad dreams. But the high dosage needed with most children make Benadryl not as useful a drug to use in these cases as other newer drugs.

Benzedrine (dl-amphetamine sulphate) and *Dexedrine* (d-amphetamine sulphate) are particularly effective drugs in helping children who have been showing the hyperkinetic syndrome: jittery, impulsive, often quite aggressive, and easily upset and frustrated. By reducing and managing such behavior, the drugs can significantly improve a child's school performance and general personality. He no longer feels *driven* to argue or fight over every trifle, as he used to do. One 10-year-old boy improved so much in a few weeks that his mother said she was sure the medicine was boosting his IQ! "He behaves more intelligently now. . . ."

Atarax (hydroxyzine hydrochloride) and *Vistaril* (hydroxyzine pamoate) are quite alike in nature, simply being different salts of hydroxyzine. Both drugs are excellent for use with jittery and upset children as well as grownups. Atarax and Vistaril are remarkably free from what are known as *spill-over* tendencies, so the physician can employ them to reduce anxiety, aggitation, and tension without incurring motor side-effects, depression, or *cloud-nine* reactions (euphoria, in medical parlance). The drugs thus are quite helpful with many children who are apt to react by emotional upheaval when things are going badly at home or in school.

Hydroxyzine appears to enable limbic and hypothalamic regions of the brain to do a little better job of managing old fight-or-flight reactions, with no perceptible effects on the thought pathways in the cerebral cortex. Nearly a billion doses have been given, with no reports of liver or blood toxicity.

Valium (diazepam), a new benzodiazepine derivative, is being used with good results with some children who show severe anxiety in stressful situations. The drug relieves muscle tension and spasms, such as seen in children who suffer from cerebral palsy. Physicians do not use Valium with young children, or in cases where the child has been convulsive. In light dosage, there is little danger of side-effects with older girls and boys.

Compazine (prochlorperazine) has had wide use with children under medical care for anxiety, hyperkinetic behavior, and mild confusion. These symptoms are seen in many children who have sustained brain injury, with or without excessive neurotic behavior overlays.

The drug is helpful in treating children who feel vomity at times, especially when anxious or excited. One third-grader I remember used to have to rush for the wastebasket whenever he had struggled with spelling or arithmetic awhile. These subjects made him feel more jittery than he usually was. The family physician changed the picture with Compazine in mild dosage four times a day. In a year the boy became a happier lad, and has been getting along far better since then. Sometimes he still needs medication, and still feels "just a little nervous" at moments. But the clinical picture has greatly changed for him, since the days before he had any medical help for the deeper neurological problem. He is in junior high now and receiving passing marks even in math and language.

Stelazine (trifluoperazine) is another of the newer drugs designed with children in mind who are very anxious, whether they react to the anxiety through agitation and hyperactivity or through general listlessness and apathy. Stelazine has little sedative effect, and does not dull mental alertness. It has been very helpful in enabling children to recover from illnesses that involved severe anxiety and emotional stress, as many diseases can do. The drug has been used with a wide demonstrated level of safety, particularly in the smaller dosage ordinarily given to children.

Mellaril (thioridazine) is useful with many children who show even severe behavior problems with psychotic-like aspects. The drug seems to act much like other phenothiazines, but without the dangerous side-effects of some of these compounds. It effectively reduces anxiety and depression and clears confusion in children who have been engrossed in jittery behavior a long time. The drug does not dull general alertness or school ability. Within a few weeks, on moderate dosage, most children show marked improvement in behavior and attitude toward themselves as well as others.

Tofranil (imipramine hydrochloride) has been proving very useful in conjunction with psychotherapy with adolescents who are depressive or despondent about themselves. In mild dosage, the drug still helps to relieve feelings of hopelessness and helplessness. Secret thoughts of suicide tend to abate, and better psychotherapeutic relationships are possible. Toxic side-effects with mild dosage are uncommon.

Suvren (captodiame hydrochloride) is a nonhypnotic stabilizer designed to help a child be less anxious and less tense—calmer, more relaxed, yet alert and not drowsy. It is a relatively slow acting drug, moderate in effect, very helpful with hyperactive children suffering from minimal brain damage. Physicians have reported Suvren to be a good adjunct drug to Chlorpromazine. To some children, it may taste bitter or metallic, but this can be controlled in most cases by reducing the dosage and insuring that the medication is taken during meals. As with many drugs, high dosage over a long period of time requires the careful checking that all good physicians do, to avert liver complications. In the usual small dosage levels, there is no danger.

Proper medication can be a most important aid in the treatment of jittery or apprehensive children, whether or not they show clear signs of brain damage. However, because children vary in response to any drug and dosage, a period of experimentation is often necessary to reach the best combination. The teacher and parent can greatly contribute to the physician's knowledge here, by keeping an exact, detailed log of the child's day-to-day reactions. Most physicians appreciate this kind of cooperation.

A complete list of all the drugs now available for helping children who are hyperactive and have perceptual-motor difficulties in school would encompass a special text in itself. Those briefly noted above were intended simply to scan the field and note some drugs that are often used with such children. By the time this book has been published, many newer, more effective drugs will have been designed in the research laboratories of pharmaceutical companies. Some of these drugs may begin to surpass many now in use, in safety and in real effectiveness. Chemists now hard at work on new drugs for psychotherapy surely will be unlocking many present secrets and puzzles. We have hardly reached the zenith of such research and design; in fact we have barely begun.

Ritalin (methylphenidate) is one of these new drugs that has been showing very good results with many jittery youngsters. Recent extensive studies of children using Ritalin are emphasizing the advantages of such *stimulants* in calming down hyperactive and inattentive children. A few years ago such uses of stimulants would have been thought quite beyond the range of good medical theory. Now these new and amazingly helpful drugs are opening even more intensive research into such pharmacotherapeutic possibilities. Our biochemist allies may yet be the long hoped for discoverers of ways to get around the old problems of hyperirritable central nervous systems that plague so many of us. Ritalin appears to be doing this very well for many children, enabling them to even cope with the visual tension problems of the classroom.

Whatever the progress in pharmacology, the most effective drugs will still need to be used in wise and intelligent combination with excellent teaching techniques, if jittery children are really to be helped to learn better and become happier persons.

The warm understanding of good teachers—and parents—still is a powerful factor in the equation, with any child. Upon this foundation of mutual respect between the child and all those who are trying to help him, the new drugs may well come to have near-miraculous effects in many cases. There are marvelous hopes ahead for such children, if we dare to enlist all possible aids right now to reach these goals.

13

PARENTS NEED
WISE SUPPORT
AND THERAPY TOO . . .

Children who have felt discouraged and upset very long are almost certain to develop emotional complications on top of whatever the deeper problem may be. This would surprise no parent or teacher who can remember facing any longstanding difficulty, particularly in school. Children who inherently are easily upset need extra care and support in the learning situation, if they are to keep on trying to do their best. Every good school has recognized this a long time.

Parents of children who are having difficulty in school have not always been offered such support and help to go on trying to do their best for their youngsters. For too many years, fathers and mothers in general have been blamed for everything that seemed to be wrong with boys and girls who were floundering in school. Such blaming has done nothing to enhance our real insight and understanding of these children. They have had to struggle alone in many cases, while grownups argued and blamed each other for failing to do something to help.

Michael's parents said they were so confused and disheartened about the boy that they had just stopped looking for help. Eight-year-old, handsome Michael had been injured enough in a rough bout with measles when he was only four that he behaved as though he were retarded at times. Yet anybody who took time to play or work with the boy soon discovered that much of his difficulty in learning centered in hyperactivity and perceptual disturbances. An older brother and sister were advancing very well in their classes, quite in line with what might be reasonably expected of children in this particular family. Then there was Michael!

By third grade he was presenting so many problems so many days of the week that the psychologist was asked to see the boy and the parents. The boy showed many clinical signs of possible organicity, overlaid by obvious emotional reactions and jittery behavior that there was little wonder why both the mother and father secretly felt trapped and hopeless about the situation. Michael's mother actually looked as *lost* as she said she felt.

Fortunately, the school nurse was a jewel in handling such cases. The junior high counselor—an ably trained and experienced man—often was in Michael's school building, working with fifth and sixth grade groups in good preparation for moving along to junior high sections. He was interested in Michael's complex problems and accepted the psychologist's invitation to talk with the parents.

The supportive conferences were so successful therapeutically with Michael's mother and father that the school district set up ways and means to offer similar services to other parents. The psychologist and school physician, in consultation with the principal and teachers, listed parents who might be most open to the right kind of supportive therapy. Many of these parents said they wanted such help, so the program was initiated. Groups of the parents—mostly mothers, though some fathers were able to arrange time to come—met to discuss all kinds of children, including children like their own.

Through many years of close association with parents of children who showed all degrees of cerebral dysfunction or damage, I discovered how few of these mothers and fathers were able at first to let anyone tell them their child ever had such a problem. Only gradually were they able to come to accept the fact of neurological involvement with enough courage and calmness to let someone try to help in good ways. These parents secretly felt hurt, even when few outsiders guessed or noticed. But I remember hundreds of these same parents who gradually did let someone help them *wade through* stages of deep hurt and shock, then into honest exploration, and finally into learning how to accept the limitations of the child.

Sometimes this took months of support by the teachers, the school physician, the nurse, the counselor, the principal, *and other mothers and fathers who had learned how to navigate such stormy waters.* In two years we built a sturdy-hearted *crew* of parent helpers who were invaluable with other parents who secretly felt terribly hurt about their children. As a team, the teacher, the physician, the nurse, the counselor, a skilled and experienced parent, and the psychologist set the stage for several miracles of new courage and even newer hope that had realistic dimensions. Out of these team experiences, incidentally, came nearly all of the ideas in these chapters.

Wise parent counseling is far from easy. It can never be done in a breezy off-the-cuff manner. The deeply hurt mother or father will either run away from such *help* or stand and fight it with sharp criticism and refusal. The therapist does not have to shed salty tears to make a parent feel understood and supported. Indeed, such an emotional display might make a parent distrust the strength and wisdom of the therapist.

The job takes something far more difficult than tearful eyes or tone of voice. Genuine understanding takes thoughtful insight; such insight is never easily come by. I have long believed that every teacher should have had an exacting training period in an excellently staffed children's clinic where the psychiatrist, psychologist, and social worker had time to lead such a weekly seminar to promote good insight. Certainly every counselor and school nurse would benefit by such an experience *before* working in a school setting. No textbook-lecture course can substitute for experience gained in the real life situation of a busy child guidance center, particularly one that is right in the middle of a teaching hospital for unhappy and discouraged children.

Two summer sessions spent *actively* in such a hospital/clinic atmosphere are likely to boost real insight and understanding far more than two or three years of course work alone. Sensing the secret agony of a parent and child as they tell *you* how they feel about themselves and their failures makes the theoretical course work come alive in the only way it can come alive—by actual contact with flesh-and-blood people. Would you trust a surgeon to operate on you who had had excellent theory courses but no exacting internship? Counselors (and teachers too, I believe) ought to have the same kind of exacting *preservice* internship training and screening. Children's lives are surely this precious.

A hidden aspect of many parents' personal struggle in coming to accept the facts about a child with brain damage is simple enough to the rest of us to admit. When the emotional overlay and annoying behavior problems with the youngster begin to diminish and smooth out with therapy, the *residue of organicity* remains. This basic part of the child's difficulty may remain a long time. As the parents gradually begin to recognize this, they feel dashed on the sharp rocks of secret despair all over again. I have seen this happen many times with parents of children I knew.

In five months in an excellent special class, Marjorie was behaving so much better that we felt the child could move to the regular class in a few weeks. She was not able to read any better than before, but the regular class group had other children with reading problems, and they were getting along happily enough in the group. Marjorie's mother misunderstood the note the teacher sent home, and came to school greatly elated that the child was "practically up to normal again." The teacher wisely called the psychologist and counselor to help with the delicate task of encouraging the mother while giving

206

her an opportunity to say how long she had hoped for such a miracle—and how she knew in her heart "there are no such miracles any more. . . ." More than a year passed before this mother was able to see that a marvelous change had come to her dear child.

Marjorie has learned many skills we once thought she might never do very well. At twenty she is a fine young woman and supports herself in a job she likes in a large store. Reading has always been a rough task for her, but her mother knows it is not as *terribly important* as she used to tell us it was for Marjorie. From my vantage point, I can look back and see the bright threads of the real miracles that did begin to weave into the sturdy fabric of the girl's life, and still are forming a wonderful part of the pattern.

Some children who do very poorly in school often are growing up in, *and frequently belong to,* community cultures that simply do not believe in (or value) education, independence, or personal achievement. These children have the multiple handicap of overcoming whatever inherent organic defects may be throwing them in school, plus the additional problem of offsetting the cultural lag of the community and of the home. Little wonder these girls and boys—and their mothers and fathers—sometimes resist the usual efforts of able teachers and counselors who might help. Aldous Huxley had the keen insight to see how readily many people accept and are willing to live by "old erroneous ideas that have fossilized into dogmas."

Such high premiums have been placed on standard achievement in regular classes in recent years that many otherwise intelligent and sensible parents are unable to accept a child who, for any reason, does not perform according to the standard schedule. Warmly supporting these parents while quietly encouraging them *not* to rush to find special tutors, buy new books advertised as sure cures for school trouble, or nag and scold the child every night to "do better, work harder, you must pass," has never been an easy task. It takes an experienced teacher, counselor, and principal. The psychologist, however wise he may be, cannot do the job alone. Neither can he do it in an atmosphere where other school staff members undercut him in any way by chance remarks to the parent or the youngster.

Chester Bowles, when he was our ambassador to India during a very troubled era in our own relationship with that emerging nation, put it poignantly enough in his *Ambassador's Report* (New York: Harper and Brothers, 1954). He was quoting the comments of one of the Point Four workers in India at the time, to illustrate the importance of the feelings of each of us when we are trying to help someone else. ". . . If the village worker is genuinely interested in helping the people, if he treats them like men who are equal with him, if he respects their opinions and ideas and does not even secretly look down upon them, then he can accomplish wonderful things. . . ."

Parents with the kinds of children these chapters have been considering sometimes are barraged by so much advice *from so many quarters* that they have a right to say they feel confused. Suppose you are the parent, and you have been sincerely seeking help with your child. How would you be inclined to react to advice from two or three sources that began to seem diametrically opposite? Suppose one person you have moderately good reason to trust says:

"Let your child swim for himself or sink. He has to learn to meet life face forward, for himself, you know." Another person says:

"That would be very unwise, every child needs a lot of help and guidance—even when he isn't fully open to it."

"Come on now, aren't you overprotecting the youngster until he has begun to feel almost smothered by your love?"

"Love him more, even when he has been bad. If you don't the unhappy child will keep on feeling rejected and unvalued."

"But why are you so lax with that child? This can impair him for years ahead."

"Such repression certainly brings serious emotional conflicts in practically any child."

"Why don't you study up on the new methods the schools are using in your child's grade, so you can help sensibly with the homework situation?"

"Stay out of that muddle, you will only make the situation worse if you don't."

Many parents have felt terrifically confused by such advice. Certainly the points of view seem wide apart at first hearing. Carefully examined, in light of the specific child's case, even these apparently opposite viewpoints really are not so wide apart as they seemed in the beginning.

For there is a *delicate balance* between overprotecting a child and rejecting him; between strictly reining him in and giving him total freedom; between ruling him autocratically and applying more democratic attitudes and principles.

The right balance is not easily attained—or kept—in the family milieu. Parents' own personalities are important factors in the dynamics. The equation is one of constant change and interchange.

Children are reared in the home, combined with the school and the community. How these agencies interweave, to produce the whole world of a particular child has much to do with how this girl or boy develops. Stress and pressure in one of these areas of the child's life may bring wide repercussions in the others. Busy parents sometimes miss this fact of life about their children.

It is easy for anyone, parents as well as teachers, to expect children to do better in school than they are truly able to do. Even the best of parents might expect the child to overcome some handicaps that are still beyond the youngster's power to manage. This is often the case with physically attractive children who have suffered subtle brain damage that has left few direct behavior problems but considerable school difficulty. "Why does such a nice looking, well-behaved girl as Kathy have so much trouble in school? No wonder her parents feel provoked at the situation. They have had all their hopes and plans for the girl upset. . . ."

Gradually enabling parents to taper their expectations for a child so these hopes are more in line with reality is no easy task, in some cases. This I well know from experience as the psychologist in school systems for many years. Mothers and fathers alike tend to resist the full truth about their children.

Yet all this has not always been bad, for it has made many schools carefully think through the deeper problems of why so many children have failed in certain kinds of school situations and not in others. Schools have needed such prodding.

To be effective in helping parents, the teacher does not have to possess clear-cut answers to every question that may arise in the conferences. This would be impossible anyway. No one is that omnipotent, or that omniscient, however wise and understanding.

The best conferences with parents are ones where parents can feel sufficiently at ease to talk frankly about their real feelings, hopes, discouragements, frustrations, fears, and even about their angry feelings. This kind of rapport may require many conferences to establish with some parents. In other cases, even where the child has been presenting severe problems in school or at home, the parents may be able to talk about the matter with warm honesty almost from the beginning because the teacher knows how to help.

The wise teacher has come to realize that it is much kinder and more potentially constructive to be frank about a child's real progress. Sugar-coating the child's failures swiftly complicates the situation. Yet every parent needs to be undergirded at times. Each of us has secret vested interests in himself. These vested interests can make us very defensive when we feel threatened.

Such defense feelings can soon block and distort clear thinking about ourselves and how we have been reacting. This is why no parent-teacher conference can be hopefully productive when either the parent or teacher feels threatened. The successful conference is set in an atmosphere of mutual respect and understanding, with open two-way communication about all facets of the problem. When the child is in the conference too, he also must feel free to say how he has been feeling about his situation. The child's participation in good conferences about him can bring many valuable gains in better attitudes and reactions. Children need to discover how human we are, and that we are neither infallible nor omnipotent. They need to know that we are mature enough to admit this freely, without losing face.

Good parent-teacher conferences, sometimes with the child present, can do this. I have watched it happening a thousand times. Such conferences surpass extensive notes to the parent, return notes to the teacher, and telephone haggling sessions.

Parents and children in our modern culture in most American communities are very conscious of such matters as grade placement, school achievement, promotion, and graduation. In most family circles, whether the parents will admit it or not, these are the status symbols that must somehow be attained, at any cost. Whatever threatens the family, in any of these status spheres, can make parents and children adopt all sorts of defenses.

"What we need in our schools is better teaching, not more special classes," a perturbed board member told me once. Her own youngster was not progressing very well and should have been moved to a good special class for a year or two. These parents pulled up roots and moved to another city, in an effort to have some school accept their child in a *regular class group*. The mother's false pride kept her from letting anyone really help. Such mothers and fathers do exist. Most teachers have faced conferences with parents who simply are not ready to let someone help who knows what to do.

Arguing with such a parent is a waste of energy and effort. Teachers are wiser to try to help in cases where better acceptance, insight, and cooperation are possible to elicit and develop. In all the schools where I served as the psychologist, we refused to pressure a parent into letting the child be placed in a special class. These classes were offered as an excellent opportunity for some children to advance better. Placing a child in such a group completely against the will of the parent would have made matters much worse for the child in most instances. He might have had to come home to such confrontations as, "Well, what did they teach you today in that stupid class?" Or, "Are you still as dumb as you were?"

Such a child, living in such a family, would find less agony of spirit in staying in the regular class, with a teacher who has some talent with slower-learners who need special methods.

The teacher need not reproach such mothers or fathers for their lack of insight. If schools everywhere had been doing a better job of helping all children, there would be fewer parents now who react hostilely to suggestions to place their children in some kind of special classes. The very names given officially to these classes in some school communities have reflected terrifically poor thinking by administrators and teachers:

— the ungraded class
— the slow-learner group
— class for trainable children
— the nonreaders class
— the orthogenic class

Children always know how well they are progressing in school. Parents always know—at least secretly—how well their children are coming along in important areas of development. Children and parents alike know their limitations fairly well. This intimate knowledge of ourselves can be heavy enough to bear at times, as any youngster could tell us. "I've known all along how whacky my brain really is, I often wished I was born different, but here I am. What can I do about it now?" an unhappy 11-year-old blurted out to me one day. Her teacher had felt sure the youngster had not guessed how poorly she rated on the special tests the week before.

Every child has inner ways of knowing such things, or cleverly guessing, after catching a few words or gestures here and there from grownups. Children are not easily fooled on important matters about themselves. They can be quietly suspicious, and they frequently surmise the truth beneath even the praise that was intended to offset the pain of facts.

Parents have keener ways of sensing the truth about their children. Discerning teachers are quite aware of all this, and do not employ false praise about a child to try to lead the parents away from the facts. "Don't worry, mother, your child is having trouble now in first grade. But I know there's nothing wrong with him in any way. He will be doing all right a year from now." "Will he, really, teacher? Are you certain about that in your own heart?" I asked the teacher after the mother had left. The teacher confessed that she doubted whether the child would be much better several years ahead.

Only the truth, as clearly as we can perceive it, can set us free to manage life's rough issues with much courage.

Yet how *should* parents be led to face the truth? How should the truth be presented? When? In what supportive atmosphere? Here are important questions that very few university courses for teachers ever touch upon, even lightly.

The following guideposts have been quite serviceable for many of the teachers I have known in school communities. These pointers are offered here simply as pointers, to be wisely adapted to the needs of specific conferences with parents who are somewhat open to such help and counsel:

Go slowly

Take time to come to know the parents. Let them discover that you as the teacher are also their friend, and can be trusted. The first conference does not have to aim to resolve every problem that has come into view about the child. The best theme for the initial conferences with any parents might well be the warmly insightful words of the tune, *Getting to Know You*. Richard Rogers and Oscar Hammerstein did a beautiful job with the music, but the lyrics are even more beautiful, with real meaning for good teacher-parent meetings:

"Getting to know you, getting to know all about you,
Getting to like you, hoping that you will like me too. . . .
Haven't you noticed, suddenly I am bright and breezy
Because of all the beautiful and new
Things I am learning about you
Day by day. . . ."

Elicit sincerity by being sincere

Good gardeners know how to persuade old trees to accept new wood. It is an art, perhaps a scientific one, but it can be learned and developed. Teachers who are available, open, and hopeful in healthy ways about children as they really are, stand in the best place to encourage parents to be open in good ways too.

Look out level

Take the parent as a valued equal. Let the mother or father see that you are not viewing him from an ivory tower vantage-point. Even the poorest parent still needs this lift, and probably will respond by more genuine effort to cooperate.

Talk about the child's good points

Encourage the parent to do this too. There are many wonderful aspects of any boy or girl, no matter what the problems have been. Put these facets into sharp focus; they can provide foundations for clearer insight into the difficulties.

Keep a larger view of the child

Sidestep any temptation to recite lists of trivia. Rather, try to help the parent to perceive the child's *deeper needs* that have been finding surface expression perhaps in antics, feigned lethargy, stubborn behavior, and so on.

"As a thoughtful parent, what do you think might be pressing the child to behave as he does some days at home or in school?"

214

"How do you think we can get together in setting a happier situation for the child to learn to behave in new ways?"
Such questions are apt to gain far more cooperation than simply telling the parent that the child won't pass or needs to be in a special class.

Carefully interpret the child's school progress

Do not talk about IQ ratings, standard test scores, or comparative data on the child. Such data, even if they were very reliable and valid (as they probably are *not!*), are not truly helpful to most parents. How Janie or Tommy are getting along within a certain group of children may reflect more on poor grouping than on the youngster. Ratings on the most reliable tests still may leave wide space for better information on the child. *IQ* scores have no place in any discussion with a parent.

Talk about effective ways the school can help this child

Ask the parent what might help. Every mother and father has such ideas. Expressing them in the right atmosphere will do much to clarify the child's situation. "What Ted needs is a good tutor. We want to get one if we can," a father or mother may say openly, at last. These feelings are better expressed than kept hidden. The wise teacher and principal can now say, "Yes, several of our staff are specialists in helping children with Ted's difficulties. How about asking one of them to help us for awhile?"

Keep the doors wide open

This is so important that it cannot be overemphasized. Good two-way communication between the home and the school has cleared up problems that had seemed beyond any kind of help. Good teachers have always known this. They also know how to keep such communications from becoming just *nuisances*.

Open doors for other help whenever necessary

Call in the school physician and nurse, the psychologist and counsellor, and the principal to join the team. Compare professional notes. Seek the best possible suggestions. Combine all the skills available to help the child and the parent.

Hold on to long range hope for every child

The right hope, realistically founded, has a place in every parent-teacher conference about a child. Often such hope is best expressed through the warmth and interest the school displays toward children and parents, rather than in words. Children are expert at reading the true meaning of warm, genuine, healthy interest in them. So are mothers and fathers.

In Summary

Take time. Be available, open, sincere, warm, insightful, encouraging, and practical. See down the years clearly and hopefully. Sense the marvelous fact of life that when we do the best we can about something, God adds his *plus* to make our best *sufficient!*

14

EARLY RECOGNITION CAN AVERT SOME COMPLICATIONS . . .

The right intervention with children who may be headed for school difficulty, *applied early enough,* can sidestep trouble that might be impossible to untangle later.

Fifth-graders are easier to pull out of impending school trouble than eighth or tenth-graders. First-graders and pre-school youngsters are easier to help than third-graders who have been feeling quite upset and discouraged about themselves

For this reason, more and more schools are devoting larger proportions of their psychological and counseling services to children in primary grades. These schools are reporting marked reductions in the number of upper grade boys and girls now referred for difficult emotional problems growing out of long discouragement. As a psychologist, I have strongly advocated the wider use of such services below the sixth grade. School boards who pay enough money to attract the best psychologist available, are wise. It is preferable to get one with extensive experience *beyond the doctorate**—and then give this psychologist free reign to work hardest with children *and teachers* in the lower grades. An ounce of prevention is still worth a pound of cure.

*Excellent training and experience are worth whatever they may cost.

Teachers' attitudes toward children are the critical factors in any classroom. The mature and experienced psychologist working in the school can well afford to invest a major portion of his time and energies in offering inservice training to the teachers, especially those in elementary grades, to encourage clearer insight into the dynamics of children's behavior. When teachers understand the multifaceted bases of children's classroom behavior—physical, psychological, and social, with all the implications of each of these bases—teachers can do a far better job with all the children in their care.

The fire department's most important job is *prevention* of fires, by educating the public in matters of fire safety. The whole town might burn down while firemen rush to put out a hundred grass fires. The psychologist in any school system must make the decision to work hardest at preventing children from heading into trouble and failure. Rushing around trying to meet emergency calls to help *untangle a hundred cases that cannot really be untangled* is a poor investment of energy and skill, even though it may seem dramatic. The first task will demand considerably more wisdom about life in general, and about schools and teachers and parents and children in particular, than the latter job. But the first task will pay greater dividends eventually, if not at the start. The latter way will just leave everyone more upset and discouraged.

Fourteen-year-old Carol's tangled life would surely be an example of what we have been discussing in these chapters, particularly the sections on complicating stresses. She is an attractive midteen, rather vivacious and usually mild mannered. These attributes have kept some of her teachers from noticing her deeper and more serious problems. Carol has long been skilled at hiding her real feelings anyway; many boys and girls are, at her age.

The sixth-grade teacher noted in Carol's cumulative record that the girl "simply isn't bright enough to do any better in school. . . ." The teacher drew this conclusion from a glimpse at a group test IQ rating of 83. This score, *if reliable,* would have placed Carol near the lower edge of the middle fifty per cent of children her age.

This satisfied the math teacher. As he expressed his feelings, "obviously Carol just does not have the brainpower needed to get along well in a good math class. The girl should be urged to take less exacting courses and give up her ambition to head for nurses training." He was willing to give up trying to teach her much math.

Since early grades, Carol had secretly thought she must be retarded mentally. When she was three, her mother and father split up after many bitter quarrels. The mother did not want the little girl—at least Carol thought this was true. "I must not have been worth much or my mother would have tried to keep me somehow," she still said in a therapy session recently. The mother probably felt desperate at the time.

Perhaps in equal desperation about what to do, the distraught father placed Carol in a boarding home that was extremely rigid in controls, with scarce compassion for a little girl who felt terribly upset and lonely. Carol gradually became used to wearing shabby clothes, but not to feeling rejected and lost. There were many times when she went to bed with only a meager supper because she had been naughty somehow. There were too many nights when she wanted to run so far away that there could be no returning. This situation went on for three years. It probably seemed more like a century to her.

Meanwhile, her father remarried and there was a new baby. Carol knew about all this, and dearly wanted to come home with her father and the new family, but the parents kept postponing this move for another two years. This upset the child very much, though she had to hide her fears and anxiety. When she was six and a half, she came home to the *new* family. By this time, however, Carol was a troubled child indeed. "Many nights I cried myself to sleep, wondering why I was being punished so bad. I used to cry in school when the teacher was nice to another boy or girl; somehow I felt afraid all over again. Often I didn't want to eat lunch, I felt so lonely, even with all the kids around."

By thirteen, the girl was so discouraged that the signs were plain enough to all her teachers. The school could have done more to try to help her then. She needed wise counseling and probably would have accepted it. Such care is quite within the range of service that every good school should offer all the boys and girls who go there. The right word of help at the moment it is needed is worth a thousand times the effort later. Too late, the best help may be of little use.

Carol nearly proved this when, in desperation, she finally ran away from home. A week later, she was returned by the state police. A wise juvenile court decided the girl needed careful diagnosis and treatment where a team of skilled professional persons would do an excellent job. Most of her previous school records were of little value, since they merely rated her in various subjects instead of attempting to find some clearer answers to why the girl was so moody and discouraged.

Within the next two months, she was given a thorough examination and was checked on important physical, emotional, intellectual, and social facets of her makeup. The neurological examination turned up some hints of possible organicity beneath Carol's apparent *jittery nerves* at moments. A careful electroencephalograph study seemed in order. The first recording was not clearly definitive, but the second one, a week later, was clear enough for diagnostic purposes.

The EEG interpretation—*cortical irritability*—was in line with my own feeling, as the psychologist, that Carol probably had been struggling along for years with an undercurrent of subtle cerebral difficulties covered over by many emotional problems. The combination probably had been very difficult to bear many times in her life.

At least much of this seemed to make better sense in trying to understand why schoolwork, particularly reading, math, and science, had been so hard for her some semesters. Perhaps, the counselor and teacher believed, her unhappiness at

Typical section of Carol's EEG tracing, recorded from cranial area over left parietal cortex. The left temporal tracing showed equally sharp spikes and dysrhythmia. Unusually high voltage electrical activity throughout extensive cortical area, especially when she was breathing deeply to produce hyperventilation for half a minute. Erratic frequency disturbances were noticed through nearly the whole record, from all cranial leads, even when she was resting quietly.

The physician-electroencephalographer interpreted her tracings to indicate that Carol's brain was often hyperirritable and stormy.

The neurologist who had examined Carol had said much the same about her: "Soft signs of cerebral injury, perhaps at birth, that have been gradually clearing a little." Her father remembered the obstetrician telling him that Carol's birth had been very difficult.

Children like Carol can be encouraged to face their moments of jittery feelings with less of the old fears and anxiety. The earlier such support and therapy is offered, the more effective it can be to the youngster.

home was part of the deeper causes too. But there were other factors too, beyond whatever desire the girl might have had to use school failure to balance old scores against her parents.

Perhaps the irritable cortical reaction that her EEG tracings revealed had been a large factor in the clinical picture of the personality difficulties she had had since she was a little girl. The bitter stresses that came at separation from her parents at such an early age may even have caused part of the chronic touchiness. For many years I have felt that this could be so in many children I have known who also suffered subtle brain injury in their young lives.

Whatever the real cause, or causes, in her case, there were clear signs that her *tendency to explode* had long been a part of her behavior picture, with no one being fully aware of it. Yet this seemed to be news to Carol when we first talked about it. With signs of considerable relief, she said, "Now I can understand why I am so touchy sometimes. I used to think I was some sort of nut, I felt so cranky." Gradually she came to see that part of her irritability and moodiness could have come out of her earlier discouragement.

On the Wechsler Intelligence Scale, she rated much above average on several subtests, reflecting her high potentials, particularly in comprehension, vocabulary, abstractions, and general information. Her markedly poor showing on the arithmetic, digit span, and block design subtests—especially in view of her excellent comprehension level—pointed to possible organicity. There were no bizarre signals in any of her responses to suggest a schizophrenic overlay. Her test performance predicted quite closely the progress she has made in a year.

In social maturity Carol now rates at least up to par for her age. Her general ability to handle considerable stress in everyday situations actually has been amazingly good. She ran away only after years of great discouragement. Even then she managed to steer clear of tragic complications that might have wrecked her life and terribly hurt her parents. For a 14-year-old out of a far-from-happy household, she has often shown

222

what would have to be called rugged courage and self-control.

One day when she seemed to be in a happy and confident frame of mind about herself, I suggested that we recheck her on the WISC. The subtest *scaled* scores were enlightening:

Vocabulary	13	Picture completion	9
Information	12	Picture arrangement	11
Comprehension	15	Block design	7
Similarities	15	Object assembly	5
Arithmetic	8	Coding	10
(Digit span	10)	(Mazes	8)
Verbal IQ level:	116	*Performance* IQ level:	90

In recent years, experienced clinical psychologists have recognized the advantages of the WISC for analysis and assessment of personality dynamics and organization. Such analysis of the directly expressive aspects of a youngster's test responses —how the child responds, behaves, and adjusts—can throw considerable light on how the boy or girl feels about important matters. Many glimpses of the underlying and supporting personality structure are possible in an extensive testing situation.

Carol's superior vocabulary subtest score was an indication of above average concept formation and general understanding. (Scaled scores of 10 are average for any age level.)

Her responses to comprehension and similarities subtests of the scale, pointed to excellent integrative ability, with fairly mature thinking ability. While her arithmetic subtest responses showed difficulty in dealing with number concepts, there were no signs of truly impaired judgement. On the picture arrangement subtest, she revealed good social insight and judgement, quite in line with her better potentials.

Her very poor rating on the block design and object assembly parts of the scale (visuo-perceptual *performance* subtests)— especially in light of her excellent showing on the predominantly *verbal* subtests — reflected possible subtle dysfunction somewhere in the right cerebral hemisphere.*

*Note Chapter 2: page 33.

64% actual size

One of Carol's most definitive sketches of herself when she first came to the children's center for special therapy.

She was 14 then, and quite discouraged about herself. Though she assured me she would not run away again, I wondered when she might do it anyway.

For a 14-year-old with no formal training in figure drawing, her sketches of herself still revealed considerable talent. On the Goodenough-Harris scale, this sketch rated comparably with her best verbal subtest scores on the WISC (About 130 IQ).

Some of her deeper feelings about herself were reflected in the sketch, and were supported firmly enough by other clinical data about her.

There were signs that she felt threatened by her developing sexuality. Many midteen girls do feel like this, even when they insist they have no such anxiety.

There were signs in the sketch that she felt confused about her true role in life: Whether to go on trying to be a tomboy, or to grow up into a healthy young woman. Whether to go on being quite narcissistic (and perhaps somewhat homosexually inclined), or to become a real woman in nature as well as in body.

Such conflicts have never been easily resolved. Carol's sketch of herself reflected some phases of the inner battle.

75% actual size

Midteen years truly are a time of *metamorphosis*. The Greeks intended the word to mean *bringing into new form*. The active years from around 11 to 16 certainly do bring new form, not only of body but also of intellect and outlook. New insights suddenly appear, almost overnight. Inner balances and controls begin to operate with less frustration. Plans about the future are more practical while still hopeful in good ways. There are increasing hints of new and genuine wisdom developing about all of life as well as self.

By her fifteenth birthday, there were many signals of such healthy metamorphosis in Carol. Even the sketch she made of herself subtly reflected a calmer girl, who was not only accepting her role in life as a young woman but looking forward to all parts of the role with new insight and warmth. There were faint signs of the old restlessness—perhaps the old moodiness. She recognized the signs herself in the sketch. Then she said, "I will feel a lot happier someday, I've grown up so much this past year!" Perhaps she will always be a little moody at times, perhaps a little vulnerable to secret discouragement. Very bright and sensitive people sometimes are.

Children like Carol rarely are able to clear all the emotional hurdles in their lives. A subtle residue of organicity often remains to dog their young adult years and sometimes even their older years. Though I have always hoped this would not happen to any of the youngsters I have helped to take care of, all too often I have seen it happen. Perhaps this part of my own clinical experience is what really has kept me at the task of trying to find all these children early, when they are more open to the right therapeutic care.

Such a possibility would be in accord with extensive studies in recent years, by Doehring, Kløve, Rietan, and others, of children with known lateralized brain damage. It is wiser in some cases, such as Carol's, to use the phrase cerebral dysfunction. This circumvents useless argument about the location, exact extent, and cause of the suspected damage, especially in instances where supporting neurological signs are not as firm as some quarters might like diagnostically.

The sewing teacher had an interesting comment about the girl's perceptual difficulties in that class: "Carol can read so well that it is hard to believe she can have so much trouble in fitting a pattern to the material. Even the simple layout scheme on the pattern envelope doesn't seem to help her do it easily." The comment did not surprise me. I had watched Carol struggle with such problems before. I knew how hard they were for her.

In a school year of intensive classroom help, Carol has made excellent progress in regaining the right confidence and spunk to do things that used to scare the wits out of her and keep her from trying at all. Some hints of these important gains could be glimpsed in the drawings she made of herself, when she first came for help, then a year later when she was feeling much happier about herself.

Her earlier attempts to draw herself were quite immature, and narcissistic, with many erasures nearly through the paper. The figure proportions were poor, and probably reflected the secret self-discouragement and moody hopelessness. The later drawings showed something of her gains during the year, to the point where she is now able to face life with steadier confidence and purpose.

The right medication helped Carol considerably. The girl has been very cooperative with the physician in discovering what drug best manages the old anxiety and depression, to help her feel calmer and less irritable. There still are days, she says, when things seem "almost as rough as they used to be, but now I can handle such matters better. . .wish somebody had known what to do with me when I was a little girl. . . ."

How much might have been done to help Carol when she was a little girl, perhaps in first grade, no one can say with certainty now. But some teacher *should* have been discerning enough—and knowledgeable enough—to do more than just feel sorry for such a child.

There are many children like Carol and the other boys and girls we have been discussing in these chapters. Sometimes their obstreperous behavior forces someone to think about ways to change the picture. More often, however, these children do not behave so terribly. Many of them get little help until they are floundering badly in sixth or seventh grade. "Somebody must do something about Ted. This is his second trip through sixth grade, but we can't send him along to junior high, the way he behaves in reading and arithmetic periods." Somebody? Something? Well, who should do it? What? How?

Schools can no longer shrug off their rightful responsibilities for such children by saying there are no effective ways to discern them early enough to help very much. There are excellent ways even for *ordinary* classroom teachers who care about children, to spot discouraged children who may have rough perceptual-motor problems beneath secret feelings of hopelessness. And there are excellent ways to help all these children: Cruikshank, Kirk, Kephart, and a score of competent sources of inservice training for *interested* teachers are available. There is no reason for teachers to lean on the old excuse that they are not trained in special education methods. Universities all across the country have been offering good courses in this field for a long while. School physicians and psychologists stand ready to help plan and organize good special classes.

Effective medications are now available for use with children who show various degrees of *subconvulsive cerebral dysrhythmia*. Carol, the girl we were discussing a few pages ago was such a child. These children do not have to be far out of bounds to benefit greatly by drug therapy. There may be no clearly definitive neurological signs in some children who still show remarkable changes of behavior when given such a drug as Dexedrine (d-amphetamine). The old irritability gradually diminishes, anxiety and depression taper off, and school difficulties come down to manageable dimensions. These changes can seem so dramatic that even the youngster begins to feel like a new person.

The teacher's discerning eye and mind are the first observation points in such changes, in most cases. Parents are slower to perceive and react in positive ways. Administrators are not close enough to the children, in most schools, to notice clearly. The best guidance counselors are still too thinly spread to spot all the children *early enough* who need special help. Teachers often are in a good position to do this very effectively, and kindergarten and preschool teachers are in the *best* position.

Beautiful 5-year-old Cynthia was more fortunate than Carol in many ways, at least in being brought for help earlier. She certainly was a pretty child who captured everyone's heart at first glance—and then left people practically terrified by her behavior. Her presenting picture at the children's clinic in a large school system contained such phrases as:

"Severe discipline problem much of the time."

"Rebellious at home and outside."

"Very hyperactive."

"Mother says child is beyond control."

"Quite destructive."

"May have hearing deficit."

The neurologist who examined the child said he saw definite clinical signs of brain damage. The EEG report noted these signals of trouble:

Excessively variable background electrical activity.

Deficiency of rhythmic waves in normal frequency range.

Predominance of spiked waves, high voltage discharges; slow delta waves for long periods of time.

The clinical picture of Cynthia supported a diagnosis of diffuse

230

brain damage, probably at birth, clouded by many emotional problems.

Cynthia had been born to her 17-year-old mother with great labor; the baby was quite anoxic and needed to be in an incubator for two weeks. She was difficult to feed even a year later, often spitting up. She slept poorly and frequently seemed like a very angry little girl who was unable to let anyone hold her or love her. Yet her parents did love her, difficult as this must have been at moments. It never has been easy to love and understand a child, however beautiful, who at three and a half still cannot speak plainly, seems hard-of-hearing, can scream for ten minutes, is so destructive, and so aggressive. Secretly I marveled at these young parents who could show real affection for such a child. I have never been quick to wrangle with parents who seem to reject such youngsters. (How might you feel about such a child?)

Cynthia's mother brought the child for me to see when she was five and a half. There were good signs that the child was far above the ratings she had been given a few months before, in another clinic. The IQ then had seemed to be little better than 70; borderline level in intelligence. My own estimate, from listening to some of the child's *breakthrough phrases* at moments, was closer to normal or even a little above such a level. (Someone might have asked me whether I was reacting to Cynthia in a kind of halo-effect because she was such a pretty child, and not really much of a behavior problem that day with me.)

Together with her parents, the teacher who had been trying to help her, the special class teacher, the speech clinician, and school physician, we took a large part of a morning to talk about the child, and plan how to help her in school. The tentative diagnosis (cerebral dysfunction, as the probable basis for considerable perceptual-motor difficulty and emotional disturbance) was discussed, to provide a foundation for school plans that would be successful with the girl. The special education teacher's extensive experience with such jittery children enabled her to set up a program that would probably work well. The parents agreed to tie-in the home environment closely with the school program, so Cynthia would have the best chance to begin to change in important ways. So the child entered the special class in September.

The first three months were not too rough. There were fewer tempery upsets right from the start in the new group. By June, many important changes had come in Cynthia's behavior. The speech clinician was happy to report that the child was using her hearing aid very well most of the school day. Her speech was improving noticeably, and her vocabulary was increasing rapidly. It was hard to believe there had been such a problem with Cynthia a year and a half earlier.

How children may react to great discouragement depends on many complex factors, including intelligence level, social maturity, earlier training and experience, and whether they are girls or boys. This last factor of sex has often been overlooked by parents and teachers in trying to understand why certain children behave as they do under some life stresses. Differences in the sexual drives of girls and boys and how these youngsters learn to adapt to their life-roles are quite marked by mid-adolescence. Comparable emotional difficulties will press a 15-year-old girl to behave very differently from a boy the same age in our culture.

When the boy breaks over into delinquency, he is more apt to be led toward tampering with cars, vacant houses, darkened school buildings, and stores. When boys get into trouble, they tend to get into trouble that involves stealing and destroying property. Crowbars, knives, and guns easily become tools and weapons of violence in a boy's hands when he feels upset enough. His vengeance will usually be clearly expressed in what he does.

Girls are more apt to turn toward sexual behavior when they have felt discouraged and angry at the world—and they can swiftly decide to go all the way sexually, to points of no real return. Any psychiatrist or psychologist with much experience with disturbed children could write a large book about such youngsters and how they behave when they jump over the ropes into serious delinquency.

Kenneth at fifteen seemed to me to behave quite typically for boys his age, though I did worry about him when he ran away from home one day and took 14-year-old Jack along with him. Both boys had been very unhappy and discouraged about themselves for a long time. Schoolwork had been going from bad to worse. Their parents hardly seemed to care whether the boys came home or not. So they ran away. Four days later, the police picked up the pair as they came out of a store they had broken into and wrecked. Kenneth had a box of cigars—and Jack's coat pockets were stuffed with candy. The first day they had found ways to force two cigarette vending machines, and spent the money on bus fare, four movies and two meals at a diner.

When they came back to school, they were a little disappointed to discover that the other boys did not really rate the incident very high and neither Kenneth nor Jack were hailed as heroes. All this was quite in line with how boys feel about such matters.

The story was much different for 15-year-old Angela when she finally ran away with Karen, also fifteen. The girls had been friends for several months, and had confided in each other very much. Each had endured years of unhappiness in a family where the parents were miserably immature, selfish, and somewhat psychotic at times. Neither Karen nor Angela had felt wanted or truly valued at home. Their schoolwork was only fair, though both girls were bright. Angela had seemed very upset for several weeks, and the family physician had suggested special medication to try to reduce her depression and anxiety. Karen's medical history noted possible birth injury from anoxia, with convulsive episodes in preschool years.

The clinical psychologist who served Angela's school had administered the Rorschach to several of the girls in her class who seemed to be vulnerable to trouble. Angela's responses to the blots had pointed to some kind of behavioral upset—possibly sexual—in the offing, but the school was not easy to alert to such possibilities. "We have enough to do here about children who are in trouble already," the principal said. A month later, the girls ran away, and then the whole staff was afraid of what might happen to "those two unhappy kids."

A week later, they were apprehended by the police in a large city many miles away, with no money left and looking very disillusioned about the whole world. They had tried hard to find jobs in a dozen stores and restaurants, but no one believed they were as old as they insisted. Out of money and out of hope, they still had decided "never to go home . . . why go home to all the old mess?" By the time the police noticed them, they had stayed with three men at a hotel for several days. Fortunately, the men had been kinder than some might have been. Neither Karen nor Angela had been roughly treated. But neither girl felt right in any way about what had happened to them. Each showed signs of heavy guilt that needed extensive therapy to alleviate.

The school was just as wary about taking the girls back and doing a good job with them as it had been slow to sense trouble ahead, before they ran away. A good school would have reacted in wiser ways.

There are many vulnerable children like Kenneth and Jack, Karen and Angela in practically any school. Early recognition of them can make treatment far more successful. Teachers do not have to be neurologists, psychiatrists, or psychologists to spot children who ought to be referred for such evaluation. The *screening* checkup does not take much time by the specialist. It can lead to much happier lives for children who, otherwise, would have to stumble along, perhaps for several years.

Better professional rapport has been developing across the last decade between educators and people in medical fields. Able psychologists have had a part in bringing this warmer feeling of partnership, perhaps because many psychologists have contributed to important strides both in medicine-psychiatry-neurology and in education. The field of special education particularly has benefited by effective teamwork between many disciplines that used to try to work alone.

Commonly now, you can find multidiscipline teams hard at work in schools, children's clinics, and service centers. I have had the privilege of working on such teams. It is warmly challenging to see what a good team of specialists, working together in mutual respect and harmony, can do. Five alert minds working as a team can be fifty times as keen as their sum singly.

Schools in many communities are utilizing this fact to good advantage to their children. School physicians, nurses, counselors, master-teachers, psychologists, speech clinicians, social workers, and dietitians more and more are giving larger portions of their time and energy to team conferences on children who need help.

Opening these conferences to other teachers, and to parents when possible, is one of the best ways to spread high-level ideas and insight across the board. The old interdiscipline barriers preserved intradiscipline ignorance and lethargy. The new team approach encourages every member to seek the full truth; to view the child in the clearest light.

The best teaching—especially of children with any degree of cerebral dysfunction and/or emotional difficulty—is based in recognizing such underlying trouble in the child and then getting him into the best educational-therapeutic situation *for him.* Obviously, such a program must have an excellent team approach, combining the brainpower of many disciplines to help the child. The pharmacologist and dietitian, dental surgeon and allergist, speech clinician, psychiatric social worker, and opthamologist might conceivably be called to help on such a team regarding a child with complex problems. No teacher, however erudite as an educator, could be expected to know much about such interrelated yet widely diversified fields or be expert in any of them. Children are certainly complex enough—even when they are presenting only the normal ranges of behavior—to defy easy explanation or simple evaluation!

When they are upset or jittery or brain-injured, they need our finest skills and keenest insight as team members. Even then, I have seen many children who were quite baffling. (And baffled!)

Team members with specialized training in medicine, neurology, psychiatry, clinical psychology, educational psychology, and social case-work generally are most able to diagnose and evaluate the youngster's full-life needs and dynamics. Responsibility for medical-psychiatric facets of the child must rest with the physician. His training and experience are of paramount value here, as a team member. Yet he will want to call on the psychologist, counselor, therapist, and teacher too, in this task, to be sure no critical facets of the youngster's needs and reactions have been overlooked in coming to a tentative diagnosis. Prognosis, likewise, is a team problem, while still the province of the physician-psychiatrist-neurologist to clarify and state.

The master-teacher, on the other hand, is the person best able to do the job of inducing the child to grow and learn, in accord with the prescription that has been devised in careful planning sessions about the boy or girl. The counselor, orientation teacher, speech clinician, recreation specialist, and others may be very important team members along with the teacher, in this part of the task. What has been wrong with the child will, to a large extent, determine the team services that are needed at any point in the program.

Between the preliminary diagnostic phase and the actual teaching program for a child, there should be good translation, planning, and orientation phases, to assure best induction of the youngster. Schools that are *taking time* to do these things have found that they *save* time and energy.

Good interdiscipline teams in many schools have found that frequent team conferences about all the children go far to enhance the atmosphere of the whole school. Thoughtful parents

Chart showing the involvement of the *Teaching* Team and the *Medical* Team in all phases of therapy in the treatment of the children we have been discussing.

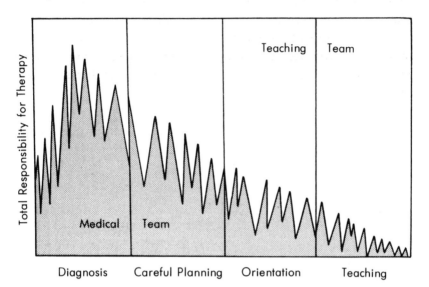

The Teaching Team consists of members with special training in teaching exceptional children. These *teaching* areas include guidance, speech correction, physical education, etc. The Medical Team includes members with special training in medicine, psychiatry, neurology, clinical psychology, educational psychology, etc.

Along the horizontal axis are the four phases involved in such a team effort. In the *Diagnosis* phase the child's full-life needs and major dynamics must be recognized, diagnosed, and evaluated. The *Careful Planning* phase has two parts. The team must first decide what facets of the total clinical picture may respond to the right therapy. Then the team must decide when and how the most effective reeducational program may promote these healthy changes and growth. In the *Orientation* phase the team must enable both the child and the parents to feel that the new program is worth the effort needed to achieve the goals. The *Teaching* phase is the actual teaching of the child in the program prescribed as being best at that time.

The chart indicates the dovetailing of the two teams in all phases. It can be seen that although all team members are involved at every stage, the *Diagnosis* phase requires that the Medical Team handle the larger part of the duties. By the time the *Teaching* phase is reached the larger part of the duties rests with the Teaching Team.

want this kind of intelligent help for their boys and girls. The right team meeting about children makes the finest kind of PTA program possible, because it teaches mothers and fathers who come how to be a little wiser, a little more human, even a little more hopeful about *themselves,* as well as about their children. I have seen this happen in many school communities where we had such team demonstrations on children's problems.

15

INTIMATIONS OF IMPORTANT BREAKTHROUGHS JUST AHEAD . . .

The inherent capacities and potentialities of the mind of man are the most amazing phenomena in the universe. No other brain than man's has such power to perceive even its own intricate functions, and to devise ways to correct its errors and compensate for its defects.

Consider, for example, the superb ability of the surgeon's brain as it enables him to relieve lethal damage in another brain so the patient gets well again. That such a brain and nervous system could develop in any creature, by whatever combination of atoms and charges, is evidence of the constant miracle that we so lightly call life.

There are many signs about us that we are more than the sum of all the cosmic dust that has gradually assembled through countless eons to compose our bodies at this particular moment in time. These signs mark the angelic heritage of every child, no matter how he happens to behave.

Four centuries before Christ, the famed Greek physician was writing down some observations on the functions of the human brain that still are startlingly correct, even in light of modern scientific insight. In his notable Volume II, devoted to lectures on elipepsy — then called "the sacred disease" — Hippocrates wrote:

"Some people believe the heart is the organ with which we think, and that it feels pain and anxiety. But this is not so. . . . Men ought to know that from the brain alone arises our sense of pleasure and joy, laughter and jest, as well as sorrow and pain, grief and tears.

"Through the brain we think and see and hear, distinguish the beautiful from the ugly, the good from the evil, the pleasant from unpleasant. . . .

"Wherefore I tell you, the brain is both the messenger and the interpreter of consciousness. . . ."

A hundred generations later, Wilder Penfield opened his now famous Vanuxem Lectures at Princeton University, in 1958, by saying that he was about to tell how he "had been listening to the humming of the mind's machinery, where the words for thinking originate. . . ." He was really bridging the centuries since Hippocrates.

By some measures of time, the span between the two men seems very great. From another view, only a brief moment has elapsed since man's own earthly beginnings perhaps ten million generations ago.

A relatively short *twenty generations ago,* in 1514, Leonardo da Vinci wrote in his biological notes, "A questo petto non batta il core," the unborn child has no need of a beating heart, because the child is *vivified and nourished completely by the life of his mother.* The human ear needed special stethoscopes not yet imagined and devised to enable it to perceive the heartbeat of the baby still unborn yet very much alive on its own powers, even at three months.

By 1677, Anton van Leeuwenhoek, the Dutch naturalist, was using his newly invented microscope to see for the first time a living male sperm cell, in a drop of seminal fluid. Here was a marvelous stride ahead in knowledge of ourselves.

Yet not until 1930, even with the development of more

powerful microscopes, were men to catch their first view of a human ova actually coming from an ovary. In 1944 came the first glimpse of the union of ova and sperm cells. Since 1955, biologists have had a clear picture of the events of the first seven days of the new infant just beginning to develop in the uterus of the mother.

Since 1960, we are starting to understand, decipher *and reintegrate* all this knowledge of human cell structures. We are beginning to grasp some of the hitherto unfathomed secrets of heredity in DNA that have shaped all human life for millions of years.

Our present generation is the very first in this long procession to have a clear picture of the course of a baby's development from a single cell to a marvelously complex individual ready to be born. Within the next fifty years—perhaps even sooner—we will uncover vital facts about ourselves that will enable us to cirvumvent many of the old causes of injury and damage to the brain and nervous system that have baffled us for a long time. This progress is heralded even now by new worldwide team cooperation between many eminent scientists from all fields of medicine, biology, neurophysiology, chemistry and pharmacology, psychiatry, psychology, and a score of newly evolving fields of electronics.

The next fifty years will see a much more complete and useful fabric of scientific knowledge of ourselves appearing. Some of the threads began thousands of years ago, while some will be just appearing tomorrow. Within the last century, especially, many illustrious names have been added to the roster of great neurological discoveries.

By 1860, Pierre Paul Broca, the noted French surgeon had discovered that lesions of the posterior portion of the third frontal convolution of the cortex were the cause of aphasias— he called them *aphemias*. This was one of the earliest scientific breakthroughs in discerning exactly what cortical areas are involved in certain disorders and dysfunctions of intelligence. Broca's work spurred the efforts of many other able biologists and physicians to understand how the brain and central nervous system carries on its intricate operations.

John Hughlings Jackson, the leading neurologist of his time, helped to carry these discoveries well into our present century. His understanding of many of the epilepsies and other brain and nerve disorders and diseases still are considered as classic in modern neurology and medicine. His death in 1911, at 76, interrupted a magnificient life of scientific genius. But he had been able to build on the discoveries of many dedicated men generations before.

Carl Wernicke, in 1875, had already laid part of these foundations, in discoveries paralleling and buttressing those of Pierre Broca a few years earlier. From Broca and Wernicke came amazingly accurate insight into the cortical areas that govern speech and verbal behavior. Looking back now, those discoveries represented giant strides.

Ferrier, just before 1890, had accurately localized the auditory center in animals, in the temporal lobe. His work helped to move the whole concept of cortical specialization forward in great leaps. Some of the early conclusions based on the discoveries up to 1900 were still only partially correct, however. Some were as inadequate and as far from the truth as the ideas of the phrenologists of the era. But this did not prevent many charlatans around the early years of the century from asserting that they could accurately describe a child's mental capacities from the shape of the skull at various places. Phrenology had a heyday for a long time. The brightest conceptions and statements of such men as Broca, Wernicke, Ferrier, and Jackson were swamped by the new craze of phrenology that explained all ability and behavior by the shape of the skull and the location of its bumps.

Then, in 1910 to 1920, a new decade of careful, painstaking research produced the background for such able biologists as Pick and Head to begin to insist that *the whole brain is in-involved in practically any of its functions, and any lesion in any area can therefore have extensive repercussions in other areas.* Here were further giant strides toward the full truth about cerebral functions.

Some researchers have had difficulty in accepting the concept of precise localization of brain function. Frederick Schiller in 1950 was suggesting a less precise localization, rather an *area-function* concept of brain function.

This concept has had considerable support in more recent years, from the studies of such neurosurgeons as Wilder Penfield and Lamar Roberts, at Montreal. Many cortical excision studies by such men have been throwing clearer light on the brain areas, especially those involved in aphasia. Results of injury or damage to many areas of the cortex are now much better understood.

It still is not possible to point to any clearly defined frontiers of cortical function. Research biologists have not been able to discover exact functional boundaries between the higher brain stem (including the thalamus) and the lower brain stem which is known to be involved in the coordination of our more primitive activities.

Nevertheless, some studies of transection through the midbrain of animals have brought important new facts to light. Sir Charles Sherrington, as early as 1904, was hard at work on this problem of function localization in the brain. He studied cats that had been carefully decerebrated—under anesthesia, of course, so the animals were completely unconscious and felt no pain.

Transection was done at the upper level of the midbrain, and the cerebrum was thus removed. When the anesthetic was removed, Sherrington found, the decerebrated animal does not really *wake up* but is an automatic motor mechanism.

He showed conclusively that, while the animal no longer appeared to think, feel, remember, or perceive the world around it, *it still could be touched into action in several ways:*

It quickly pulled its limbs away from thorns that pricked them. Milk put into the mouth was promptly swallowed. Acidy fluids were rejected, if put into the mouth. The animal could

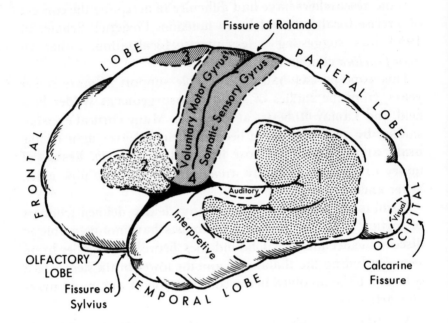

Four cortical areas in the dominant hemisphere—usually the left—play major functions in ideational speech. These specialized areas have been discovered within recent years by extensive records of necessary excisions, and by electrical *aphasic arrest* techniques employed before neurosurgery.

1. Posterior speech cortex, much as mapped by Wernicke in 1875.
   Even slight damage to this area can bring severe irreversible aphasia.
2. Anterior speech cortex, much as defined by Broca in 1885.
   Damage to this area generally brings aphasia that has been known to clear up almost completly in some cases.
3. Supplementary vocalization area, as defined by Penfield et al.
   Ablation of this area results in aphasia, but this disappears in a few weeks.
4. The motor area for speech—vocalization, lips, jaw, tongue, and throat.
   Any injury to this area will result in speech disturbances also.

Neural integration of all these areas is now believed to take place in the thalamus, through the subcortical networks in the centrencephalic system.

stand, and even walk a little, and it could still vocalize and often purred. In short, the decerebrated animal could move and adjust in automatic ways to its immediate environment.

"The mindless body," wrote Sherrington, "reacts with the automatic fatality of a multiple penny-in-the-slot machine to certain stimuli. Around the cerebrum, then," he concluded, "with its physiological and psychological attributes, must turn the main interest of biology." Here was an echo of Hippocrates' thoughts, twenty-three centuries earlier.

In more recent years, such men as Cobb, Bertrand, Jasper, and Penfield have been adding to the accumulated knowledge of how the brain functions. Through the untiring research of these scientists we now know more about cerebration than was known even by 1900. The last decade has opened the very architecture of brain and nerve cells to our view, so that scientists are beginning to understand many things about intelligence and behavior that used to be mysteries.

Clinical results of brain surgery necessitated by head injuries and infections have given opportunities to gather accurate data on localization of function. In cases, for example, where the calcarine area of one occipital lobe had to be removed, blindness ensued in the opposite field of vision.

Excision of one postcentral gyrus brings a loss of discriminatory sensation from the opposite side of the body. Removal of the precentral gyrus results in permanent paralysis of all skilled or delicate movements on the opposite side of the body, though some general movement may still remain.

This does not mean there are no additional motor and sensory areas in the cortex than these. By 1956, Bertrand had discovered several *supplementary* motor areas in the cortex that project their impulses down the spinal cord and out to some muscle groups, but with less control than the primary areas exert over the same muscles.

Neurologists now are aware of secondary somatic areas that receive impulses directly from the periphery. Lesser secondary visual areas surround the primary calcarine fissure. These secondary areas can be removed—at least on one hemisphere—with little or no loss of major function.

The other vast cortical areas have their own interconnections within the brain, enabling these areas to carry on their intricate functions. These functions can be described more as psychical, rather than sensory or motor.

All areas of the cortex are united with subcortical gray matter by means of two-way fiber projection systems. Some of these connection systems are more specific in function than others. We know this fact from the extensive studies of such men as Jasper and Penfield in the last decade, but much more needs to be discovered about these interconnecting nerve networks.

Yet out of the brilliant insight of Penfield and others, good evidence has been accruing about the whole central nervous system in man. Leading neurologists now can demonstrate a level of integration within the central nervous system—Penfield, among others, calls it "centrencephalic integration"—that transcends the level of integrative power of the cerebral cortex itself.

Important to life as is the cortex of the brain, it is still no greater in importance of function than the rest of the central nervous system that interconnects the cortex with all the organ systems in the body. In fact, the highly developed neural mechanisms within the central nervous system are often more intimately associated with the initiation of voluntary activities— and with the sensory summations prerequisite to these activities —than is the cortical area of the brain. If this were not so, all of us would soon be in trouble.

If a child did not withdraw his hand from a hot stove before the cortex itself had considered the danger and fired messages to make the muscles move, the hand might be badly injured.

All regions of the brain undoubtedly are involved in even the simplest conscious processes of our lives, as well as in the far more complicated processes. Without a brain, we would be reduced to the level of Sherrington's laboratory animals, reacting automatically to the immediate environment. The brain, intact and healthy and alert, makes possible our thoughts, our feelings, our recollections, and our percepts.

Yet there is a wider and equally indispensable substratum of consciousness that lies outside the cerebral cortex, not in the *new* brain we have gained in recent millions of years, but in the *old* brain that our most ancient ancestors had millions of years before—the brain now called the diencephalon and mesencephalon.

Any injury, however slight it might appear, to any part or region of the whole system depletes the effectiveness of the whole in some degree. This neurologically demonstrable fact of life should help us be not only wiser but kinder toward all persons who have sustained such injuries.

In his excellent and very readable text, *Treatment of the Child in Emotional Conflict,* Hyman L. Lippman frequently notes how easy it is to overlook subtle organicity in children who are behaving very badly. Many bizarre upsets and reactions in children cannot be explained by simply calling them symptoms of emotional problems. Specialists who have had intensive training that has conditioned them to look for pathologic emotions in children must keep another possibility clearly in mind: A pathologically upset central nervous system can initiate severely abnormal and bizarre behavior. Organic damage can so disrupt the child's ego that his hold on reality is threatened or even lost.

Likewise, emotional factors superimposed on extensive organicity in a child have sometimes been overlooked as part of the cause of the youngster's bad behavior. Such a mistake can easily be made when the obvious CNS pathology might account for practically all of the clinical picture. Evidence from recent studies has shown that catastrophic levels of anxiety can produce behavior aberrations quite like the clinical picture seen with brain damage. There are clinical differentials, of course.

Fortunately, the training programs of physicians, psychiatrists, neurologists, psychologists, and social workers are undergoing radical changes in many universities now, to help all these specialists understand the complex and interweaving multifacets of children much better. Special education departments of major universities now are encouraging their students to gain a practical working knowledge of all the life-sciences—neurology, biology and biochemistry, and physiology and anatomy—as bases for clearer understanding of psychology and education. These important training program changes are not coming a moment too soon, but they will have profound effects on all the fields of education, social work, medicine, and psychiatry in a generation.

These strides ahead are good. Our children's children will be able to build on these *new* foundations that have taken so long to achieve. Open-heart surgery would have been thought to be the maddest idea not long ago. Excision of epileptic foci in the cerebral cortex was *undreamed* of less than a century ago. Yet in the next fifty years, young people may be looking back and wondering why we took so long to discover and apply such marvelous life-saving knowledge and skill.

There has been a kind of divine impatience built into some men in every generation since time began. Healthy dissatisfaction with the apparent ease and perfection of *status quo* has sifted out the human mind and brain from that of lesser creatures. What seemed utterly beyond the fullest range of possibility to do a century ago may, within another swift moving century, become part of everyday accomplishment.

At the moment of each new important discovery and feat, we humanly are apt to rest on the warm pride that wells up in us about the accomplishment. How long this temporary plateau in the curve lasts depends in part on how strongly we believe we have reached the highest level of perfection. As with some children at times, many grownups are inclined to like the feeling of *having arrived* more than the vision of what needs to be done next. All of us have at least a touch of this very human pride in what we *have* done. Most of us are at least a little bit lazy when it comes to getting down to the big tasks that need to be done. We need something to move us off dead center; to make us begin to move.

Sometimes we are nudged by the right dissatisfaction, so we have to press ahead on new frontiers again. Then the temporary plateau of upward progress breaks into a new rise, in a slightly steeper angle toward perfection and away from earlier exaggerated personal lacks and errors. Each successive generation has been spurred a little more by this ancient inborn desire toward ultimate perfection.

The present year is witnessing a thousand upward surges in neuropsychiatry, medicine, surgery, and psychology aimed at helping children who suffered central nervous system injuries.

Just recently, Russian physiologist T. Pavlova, hard at work in the lab of the Academy of Medical Services, in Moscow, has been studying how dogs that were clinically dead not only can be revived, but actually regain healthy brain capacity. Several animals that had been brought to clinical death level under conditions of hypothermia — very low temperatures — have been revivified to normal intelligence and behavior in a few months. A year after clinical death from hypoxia—shortage of oxygen—Pavlova's dogs have been reflecting complete cerebral recovery. He has discovered that the dog's cerebellar (lower brain) functions are restored at a slower rate, but they are gradually restored to good levels.

Such studies are lending bright hope to hypotheses about the healing and recircuiting powers of many portions of the central nervous system. Time is becoming an intimate team member with medical and surgical techniques of treating children with some kinds of brain injuries.

Researchers Liu Shih-Yih and Wu Chin-Eh have been studying nearly two thousand children encephalographically. The children range in age from four through the late teens, and include a wide range of intellectual capacity from high to normal to retarded. Some of the findings of the study thus far are hopefully enlightening and clarifying, supporting the guesses of many earlier researchers.

Apparently the human brain develops gradually *and consecutively,* though not at the same pace for all cortical areas. Two periods of swift development seem to occur in most children: between five and six years, and later between thirteen and fifteen years. This finding certainly corroborates the feeling of many parents and teachers that kindergarteners to first-graders and junior-high schoolers are in intellectual periods of high acceleration.

This study has revealed a maturation sequence of the brain that has been hypothesized for several years: Occipital areas of the cortex come to maturity first, when the child is around nine. Temporal areas next reach maturity, around eleven. The whole cortex is quite mature by thirteen to fourteen. These findings have tremendous inferences for all teaching and school programming. For many years such physician-scientists as Wilder Penfield and Lamar Roberts have been urging schools to do more in primary grades to instill language skills in all children. Learning a new langauge after adolescence is likely to be far more difficult than in earlier years. Liu and Wu's studies are strongly supporting this modern concept.

Their research has turned brighter light on a long suspected cause of true mental slowness in some children: the EEG records of such boys and girls in the study reveal *pronounced electrical inertness.* Truly slower children may simply have brain (and nerve) cells that are inherently lower in electrical activity. The cells and nerves may be equal otherwise in quality to those of other children, but have less *electrical potential* for some reason not yet known.

With just a little imagination, the day can be envisioned not far ahead when there may be practical ways, as yet not even thought of, to give the brain cells of very slow children much better power and effectiveness. The concepts of intelligence now held so strongly in many places someday may no longer be accepted anywhere.

New advances in medicine and surgery are saving the lives of many children who used to be doomed to invalidism at best. Anesthesia is safe enough now to permit surgeons to operate on babies only a few weeks old. A newly developed electronic instrument, the fetal heart monitor, is enabling obstetricians to be sure whether an unborn infant is receiving sufficient blood through the umbilical cord during the birth process. Even slight interruption of this vital blood supply can bring brain damage or death to the infant. Warned in time by the new monitor, the physician can quickly take steps to avert such a danger or tragedy.

Every year hundreds of children in our United States have died of measles. Certain neurocerebral complications of this disease that in some circles used to be thought to be "just a benign childhood annoyance" are now recognized as leaving permanent mental defects. This fact has been spurring research on the problem of prevention.

Nearly six million children have now been immunized against measles, so these boys and girls will not be endangered by the disease. The discoveries of Dr. John F. Enders and his brilliant associates in immunology have led to the new vaccines. Years of tireless research by hundreds of medical scientists—plus millions of dollars—went into this important labor. These investments are still modest, when we consider the value of the young lives that can now be protected from needless danger.

The score or more of pharmaceutic research teams and companies that are pressing such research warmly deserve all the praise that trickles down to them once in a while for such continuing efforts. Millions of boys and girls are even now on the long lists of *unknowing* benefactors.

Special studies by such teams have been revealing high relationships between prematurity and later neurological difficulties and anomalies. Some studies are putting the percentage as high as 70% for the chance of prematurity bringing such troubles later. These findings are spurring greater research on the deeper causes of prematurity and what can be done in many instances to enable the mother to reach full term with

251

her baby. Here are coming vastly important breakthroughs for countless children who will not be hurt by premature birth.

Research evidence is mounting on certain rare forms of abnormal redblood cells in pregnant women that can be very dangerous to the babies as well as to the mothers. Early, accurate recognition of the presence of these abnormal cells is providing the margin of time so necessary in averting harm to mother and child. The ultimate results of this research will require a thousand years to evaluate fully, but many children are already benefiting.

One of the most dramatic breakthroughs in the last few years has been coming for a long time: Techniques for *early recognition* of congenital heart disease in very young children. This in turn is making effective treatment much more successful for these children.

The development of very sensitive electrocardiographs have enabled physicians to discern dangerous coronary conditions in babies only a few hours old. Corrective measures can then be taken quickly enough to prevent cerebral damage that might result from lowered oxygen supply to the brain.

These advances have been spurring new beginnings too, in a hundred areas of neurobiology. The advances of the next quarter-century may dwarf the greatest gains thus far.

Generations of children yet unborn will live to bless the long lines of men and women—*ordinary* as well as great—who have labored to make these things possible. Every good teacher belongs in this list.

GLOSSARY OF
SPECIAL TERMS . . .

with some practical meanings

for teachers and parents

a- or **an-** (ah-, ahn-) Greek: prefix, implifying separation.
Signifying without or not.

acalculia (ah kal ku le ah) Latin: *calculare,* to reckon.
Inability to do simple arithmetic calculations. Many children who show perceptual difficulties also have arithmetic trouble.

agnosia (ag no se ah) Greek: *gnosis,* perception.
Loss of power to recognize the import of sensory stimuli. More than one sensory modality may be involved: auditory, visual, tactile, olfactory, gustatory. There probably are far more children with subtle degrees of agnosia than have been recognized.

aphasia (ah fa ze ah) Greek: *phasis,* speech.
Defect or loss of power to express by speech, writing or signs. Also the loss of ability to comprehend spoken or written language. Injury or disease of brain centers for these functions may cause a child to be aphasic.

aphasic arrest
Surgical procedure of interrupting normal responses of a cortical area or center, by touching the exposed area with special electrodes. Careful studies of the human cortex by this technique—in cases where the brain was exposed for necessary surgery—have revealed many of the specialized areas such as for speech and vision. The technique is not harmful to the patient in any way.

apraxia (ah praks e ah) Greek: *prassein,* to do.
Loss of previously acquired ability to perform intricate skilled acts. Some cerebrally injured children can perform simple movements fairly well, but not complicated ones. Such children often have been misjudged as inattentive or not interested in doing any better.

253

biochemistry (bi o **kem** is tre) Greek: *bios,* life+*chemeia,* chemistry.
Pertaining to the chemistry of the living organism and its vital processes. The biochemical forces at work in even the simplest cell or nerve fiber still are exceedingly complex. But biochemists now are fathoming many of these life functions.

catalytic (kat a **lit** ik) Greek: *katalyein,* to dissolve.
Causing an alterative effect. The change is brought about by the presence of the catalyst that in itself remains stable. Somewhat in this respect, an excellent teacher is often the catalytic agent to children who have needed the right influences to feel encouraged again.

catastrophic (kat a **strof** ik) Greek: *katastrophe,* swift downturning.
Great, sudden, inclusive worsening. Very jittery children sometimes show catastrophic reactions to stress, practically *coming unglued* with fear and anxiety. Every teacher with much experience can remember such children.

CNS: central nervous system Greek: *systema,* an arrangement.
A major division of the total nervous system, consisting of the brain and the spinal cord. The rest of the total system—the *peripheral* division—includes the other nerve fibers and their end organs.

cephalocaudal (sef ah lo **kaw** dal) Greek: *kephale,* head +Latin: *cauda,* tail.
Development of the child *in utero* procedes cephalocaudally—from head to tail. A baby comes to *discover* his hands before his feet. Smooth eye-hand coordination usually comes long before eye-foot coordination.

cerebellum (sehr uh **bel** um) Latin: diminuitive of *cerebrum,* little brain.
That division of the brain behind the cerebrum and above the pons and fourth ventricle. The cerebellum is concerned in the coordination of movements.

cerebrum (**sehr** uh brum) Latin: *cerebrum,* brain.
The major portion of the brain, with two hemispheres that occupy the upper part of the cranium (Greek: skull). The cerebrum comprises the largest part of the central nervous system, weighing about 3 pounds in the average adult, or about 5/6 of the weight of the total CNS.

cholinergic (kol lin er jik) Greek: *chole,* bile+*ergon,* to make or spur
Stimulated by choline (acetylcholine). A term applied to those nerve fibers that liberate acetylcholine at a synapse (nerve junction) when an impulse passes across the junction.

clinical (klin e kl) Greek: *klinikos,* pertaining to a bed; bedside.
Related to the actual observation and treatment of patients, as distinguished from more theoretical or experimental relationships. The clinical psychologist in a school, for example, sees the child in a diag-

nostic or evaluative and/or therapist relationship. The practicing physician and psychologist thus are clinicians.

congenital (kon **jen** i tal) Latin: *congenitus,* born together.
Existing at birth, or before birth. Many children are born with subtle congenital defects of the brain and nervous system. Sometimes these defects or injuries clear up so completely that there are no discernible traces after a few years.

cortex (**kor** tex) Latin: rind.
The outer layer of any organ, as distinguished from inner portions: The cortex of the brain (*cerebri*) is composed mainly of a very thin layer of gray matter cells—the cineritious substance.

diagnosis (di ag **no** sis) Greek: *dia,* through + *gnosis,* knowledge.
The art of distinguishing one disease, defect, or disorder from another; and the determination of the nature and progress in the person.
Prognosis (Greek: foreknowledge) is the careful estimation of the prospect of recovery, as indicated by the nature and symptoms of the trouble in a particular patient.

diencephalon (di en **sef** ah lon) Greek: *di,* double + *egkephalos,* brain.
The posterior (rear) division of the prosencephalon (forebrain). This division contains the pineal or hypothalamus gland.

disinhibition (dis in hi **bish** un) Latin: *dis,* apart + *inhibere,* to restrain.
The reduction of previous restraint; or the revival of a previously extinguished reaction.

dysfunction (dis **funk** shun) Greek: *dys,* poor or difficult + Latin: *functio,* function.
Disturbance, impairment, or abnormality of functioning of any organ. **Cerebral dysfunction** has come to have better acceptance than terms such as brain damage, especially in talking to parents about a child. This is understandable to any wise teacher.

dyslexia (dis **leks** e ah) Greek: *lexis,* diction.
Inability to read understandingly, often because of a lesion somewhere in the brain. The term also may mean a condition where reading is quite labored, with marked fatigue or disagreeable sensations. Many children with subtle cerebral injury are dyslexic.

dyslogia (dis **lo** je ah) Greek: *logos,* understanding.
Impairment of reasoning power, sometimes used to mean impairment of speech, in some children with diffuse mental disorders.

dysrhythmia (dis **rith** me ah) Greek: *rhythmos,* rhythm.
Disturbance in rhythm, observed in some children with speech disorders. **EEG dysrhythmia** refers to irregular pace of the electrical waves from any area of the brain.

EEG: electroencephalogram (e lek tro en sef ah lo gram) Greek: *egkephalos,* brain+*gramma,* mark.

The graphic recording of the electric currents developed in the brain. Electrodes are applied to the scalp, over certain cortical areas. Leads from the electrodes carry the currents to high gain amplifiers that operate recorder pens marking on a moving chart. In recent years, EEG recordings have been made of cortical and subcortical areas exposed during necessary brain surgery.

emotion (e mo shun) Latin: *emovere,* to disturb.

Any degree of mental excitement or disturbance characterized by alteration of feeling tone. Jittery children frequently are emotionally upset too, showing excessive fear, anger, anxiety, and discouragement.

empathy (em pah the) Greek: *en,* in+*pathos,* feeling.

Recognition of, and entering into, the feeling of another person. Good teachers are apt to feel empathatic toward the children in their care. The only problem is how to manage such warm understanding in ways that help the child most and do not hinder him.

encephalon (en sef ah lon) Greek: *egkephalos,* brain.

(Some Greeks might have smiled at the phrase our children like to use about themselves at times: "I'm right on the ball today!" Kephale meant head. Every teacher has seen many heads that were pretty much like a ball.)

endo- (en doh-) prefix, Greek: *endon,* within.

endocrine (en doh krin) Greek: *krinein,* to secrete.

Internally secreting; as the thyroid gland does, for example.

endogenous (en **dohj** en us) Greek: *gennan,* to produce.

Growing or generating from within; originating within the organism. Endogenous toxins are poisons that are generated or liberated within an organ, by some malfunction or breakdown of the organ.

enzyme (en zim) Greek: *en,* within+ *zyme,* lighten by fermentation.

An organic compound, frequently a protein, capable of producing (by catalytic action) the splitting of some compounds into simpler substances. Each enzyme can act only upon a particular compound, at exactly the right temperature, acidity or alkalinity, or other conditions. No organism could survive without the intricate chemistry of enzymes. Slight disturbances in these vital coordinations in a child may have wide complications.

epidemiology (ep i dem e ol o je) Greek: *epidemios,* prevalence+*logos,* study.

Scientific study of the frequency, diffusion, and contagion of disease in the community. Recent studies of the incidence and causes of brain injury among children have been throwing much needed light on this vast problem.

etiology (e te ol o je) Greek: *aitia*, origin +*logos*, study.
Scientific study of causes and origins, particularly of diseases.

excision (ek sizh un) Latin: *excisio*, to cut out.
Surgical removal of tissue. Some areas of the brain can be excised now with moderate safety.

exogenous (eks oj e nus) Greek: *ex*, out of +*gennan*, to produce.
Developing or originating outside the organism. Lead would be an exogenous toxin.

febrile (feb ril) Latin: *febris*, fever.
Pertaining to fever; feverish.

focal (fo kal) Latin: *focus*, hearth (center of the household activities).
Pertaining to the center of (as the center of infection, or of injury).
Focal discharge, in an electroencephalographic record, refers to such electrical discharge activity that apparently centers in a specific area of the brain. Epileptic foci can sometimes be surgically excised, without much damage to other tissue of the cortex.

gestalt (ges tawlt) German: *gestalt,* form (usually of a group of things).
Any group or constellation of ideas that seems to come to mind as a whole more readily than as separate parts.

gyrus (ji rus) Greek: *gyros*, circle; circular portion.
A convolution of the cerebral cortex. Lesions of the angular gyrus (sharply bent convolution) of the inferior parietal lobe of the left hemisphere are known to cause asymbolia: impairment of ability to comprehend symbolic things, figures, signs. Such a lesion could markedly impair a child's ability in arithmetic as well as in reading and writing.

haptic (hap tik) Greek: *haptikos,* able to lay hold of.
Psychological meaning: Pertaining to the ability to comprehend the less visible or visually apparent aspects of something or someone. Haptic sensitivity is thus distinguished from more *visual* sensitivity. Most of us are somewhere between these poles. Great artists are apt to *sense* life haptically. Not so strangely as might first be thought, many children are able to sense how we feel toward them, even when we have tried to conceal our real feelings by smooth words and outer appearances.

histology (his tol o je) Greek: *histos*, tissue+*logos*, study.
The division of anatomy dealing with the minute structure, composition, and function of the various tissues.
Cytology (si tol o je: from the Greek *kytos,* meaning hollow vessel or anything that covers or contains) is the subdivision of histology that

concerns the scientific study of cells, their origins, structure, and function.

hyper- (hi per-) Greek: *hyper,* above.
Prefix signifying above, beyond, excessive. Hyperactive children are often quite jittery and difficult to get to pay attention.

Hypo- signifies under, beneath, deficient. Hypoxia (shortage of oxygen) at birth can subtly injure the child's brain.

hyperkinetic (hi per ki net ik) Greek: *kinesis,* motion.
Pertaining to or marked by overactivity. This term has the same meaning about jittery children as *hyperactive.*

hyperventilation (hi per ven ti la shun) Latin: *ventilare,* to fan.
Very deep breathing; utilized by the physician or neurologist in examining for suspected epilepsy or tetany (sharp flexion of the wrists and ankles, often a signal of parathyroid hypofunction or calcium deficiency). Excessive intake of O_2 (oxygen) can produce dizziness, confusion, and muscle cramp or spasm in some children. Hyperventilation while taking EEG recordings is employed to percipitate focal discharge in children with suspected epilepsy.

hysteria (his te re ah) Greek: *hystera,* uterus + *ia,* denoting some disorder or disturbance of.
In modern psychiatric parlance, the term refers to conditions that seem to be physically caused and real enough, yet are more psychogenic in nature. Hysteric signs in children are very difficult to diagnose in some cases, puzzling the best physicians and psychologists at times. The wise physician and psychologist never overlooks the possibilities of organicity beneath all such signs. (The Greeks of Hippocrates' time thought that very excitable women had a deeper uterine upset. There was considerable truth in the idea. We now are aware of how much even slight endocrine disbalances or disturbances can upset anyone, grownup or child.)

iatrogenic (i at roj en ik) Greek: *iatros,* physician+*genesis,* production.
Resulting largely from the activity of the physician or therapist. Anxious children often pick up *symptoms* from hints in the examination or treatment procedures. Good teachers need to keep this in mind, especially in working with children who are secretly discouraged about themselves. Such youngsters may not read very well, but they quickly sense our own subtle feelings of hope or hopelessness about them.

idiopathic (id e o path ik) Greek: *idios,* own or peculiar+*pathos,* disease.
Disease (or dysfunction) that somehow is self-originating, or at least. has no cause yet discovered.

Cryptogenic (Greek: *kryptikos,* hidden *genesis,* production) hence, hidden origin.

imperception (im per sep shun) Latin: *perceptio,* to perceive.

Any distortion or error in the reception of sensory impressions. Paul Schilder, of New York's famed Bellevue Hospital, had shown as early as 1930 that body image imperception may stem from cerebral lesions localized in the angular gyrus of the left hemisphere. Gross imperception difficulties may also be signals of wider regressive phenomena in intellectual functioning resulting from any kind of brain damage.

intelligence (in tel li gence) Latin: *intelligere,* to understand, comprehend.

David Wechsler has defined the term operationally: The global or aggregate capacity to act purposefully, to think rationally, and to deal effectively with the environment. Thoughtful teachers and parents find this definition quite serviceable.

in utero (u ter oh) Latin: *in,* within + *uter,* bag.

Within the uterus; still unborn.

kinesthetic (kin es thet ik) Greek: *kinesis,* motion + *aisthesis,* sensation.

Pertaining to the perception of motion, position, weight, force. Slight disturbances in any of these perceptual modalities can swiftly make a child feel terribly upset and fearful. Expert reeducative techniques are needed to enable such children to begin to feel sufficiently safe from injury to be able to go ahead with a little less fear and anxiety. Children with much of a kinesthetic problem are no cases for novices in the field of teaching.

laterality (lat er al i te) Latin: *lateralis,* side.

The tendency, particularly in carrying out motor acts, to employ the hand, foot, eye, and ear on the same side. Many children with confused laterality also show signals of brain damage, although not all such boys or girls have sustained brain injuries. Neurological immaturity may also account for poor laterality in some children. **Dominant laterality** simply refers to the preferential use of the right side (*dextrality*) or the left side (*sinistrality*).

lesion (le shun) Latin: *laesio,* a wound.

Any pathological or traumatic damage or loss of tissue.

lethal (le thal) Latin: *lethalis,* deadly.

Very dangerous to life; fatal.

lobe (lob) Greek: *lobos,* globular extension or portion.

A globular part of any organ, usually separated by boundaries, as the frontal lobes of the brain, or the lateral lobes of the thyroid.

metabolism (me tab o lizm) Greek: *metaballein,* to alter or change about.

The sum of all the biochemical processes that produce and maintain living organized substance. Also, the transformation by which energy is made available to the organism. Many of the children discussed in the chapters of this book would show complex errors of metabolism.

neuron (**nu** ron) Greek: nerve.

A complete nerve cell with all its processes, collaterals, and terminations; regarded as a structural unit of the nervous system. *Sensory* neurons transmit impulses to the cortex. *Motor* neurons carry impulses to the muscles.

neuropsychiatry (**nu** ro si **ki** ah tre) Greek: *psyche,* soul.

The combined branch of medicine encompassing both neurology and psychiatry.

neurosis (nu **ro** sis) Greek: nerve + *osis*, disease.

Disorder of the psychic or mental constitution, in contrast to *psychosis.* Jittery children from whatever cause, are apt to behave very neurotically at times. Neurosis is less disabling or incapacitating than psychosis.

organicity (or gan **is** i te) Greek: *organikos,* pertinent to organism.

Refers in this text to the organic bases or causes of thinking and behavior difficulty or defects. Subtle organicity in a child is not easy to discern at times. Children who are coming down with such an infection as measles, for example, may seem suddenly very irritable and cantankerous a few days before other signs of the real trouble become apparent.

para- (**par** ah-) Greek: *para,* beyond.

Prefix signifying beside, beyond, accessory to, apart, or separate from.

pathology (pah **thol** o je) Greek: *pathos,* disease + *logos,* study.

The branch of medicine that concerns the essential nature of disease, especially the structural and functional changes of tissues and organs.

perception (per **sep** shun) Latin: *perceptio,* a seeing through.

The receiving of an impression via any of the senses. The phrase *perceptual-motor-language,* as employed in this text, is intended to emphasize the intimate interrelationships between all the information-decoding (receiving-comprehending) systems and the information-encoding (expressing-reacting) systems. All these systems are highly complex. Slight imperfection or impairment of any part of a system can disrupt the whole network and cause extensive imperception. Little wonder that some children who sustained brain damage find so much difficulty in many school tasks and feel so discouraged about themselves at times.

perseveration (per sev er a shun) Latin: *perseverare,* to persist.

Continued repetition of words or motions that thus become meaningless.

260

Distinguished from *perseverance,* for example, which is the ability to stay at a task that needs doing.

pharmacology (fahr mah **kol** o je) Greek: *pharmakon,* medicine+*logos,* study.
The scientific study of drugs in all their respects.
Pharmacotherapy (Greek: *therapeia,* treatment.) treatment of disease by medicines.

poly- (**pol** e-) Greek: *polys,* many.
Combining form meaning much or many.

predisposition (**pre** dis po **zi** shun) Latin: *pre,* before + *disponere,* to dispose.
Any latent susceptibility to disease or disorder that may be activated under certain conditions or stress. Brain-injured children often are predisposed to irritability.

projection (pro **jek** shun) Latin: *pro,* before+*jacere,* to throw.
In clinical psychology: The mental mechanism by which a repressed idea or desire is disguised by being regarded as belonging to something or someone in the external world.

psychosis (si **koh** sis) Greek: *psyche,* soul.
Now applied to the deeper, more far-reaching and prolonged disorders of thinking and behaving. Children who are psychotic are very seriously ill. Psychoses frequently are based in organicity that may or may not be reparable.

rapport (ra **pohr**) French: *rapport,* harmonious relationship.
Jittery children often secretly feel suspicious of practically anyone who tries to help them, and may take a long time to feel truly safe with these persons. Establishing warm rapport with many of the children described in the chapters of this book is definitely an art. But good teachers are ingenious enough to master the art.

schizophrenia (skiz o **fre** ne ah) Greek: *schistos,* split + *phren,* mind.
Bleuler's term for *dementia praecox;* mental deteoriation from psychogenic cause, usually in younger children and adolescents. Schizophrenic children often show marked cleavage or splitting of mental functions, as distinguished from the fairly intact though somewhat ineffective thinking or behavior of neurotic youngsters at times.

sedation (se **da** shun) Latin: *sedatio,* calming.
Refers particularly to the medical process of allaying nervous excitement. Hyperactive children can be greatly helped to get along better in school as well as at home by the right sedation.

sham rage
Children with brain injury sometimes show sudden outbursts of motor

261

activity that may very closely resemble real fear or rage. Jittery children may show sham rage when the blood sugar level drops too low.

somatic (so mat ik) Greek: *somatikos,* bodily.

Pertaining to the body, particularly the framework and form, as distinguished from the viscera and their functions. Children who have been feeling very upset and discouraged sometimes show *psychosomatic* symptoms: bodily symptoms of a psychic, emotional or mental origin. The accurate diagnosis of such a youngster can be very difficult and is no task for a novice.

subcellular (sub sel u lar) Latin: *sub,* below +*cella,* compartment.

Pertaining to minute parts or functions of the cell. Subcellular electrochemical defects in structure and function are now believed to cause many of the subtle perceptual difficulties discernible in some children. *Submicroscopic* and *ultramicroscopic* simply mean too small to be visible with the microscope. The newer electron microscope can reveal subcellular structure very plainly.

subcortical (sub kor ti kal) Latin: *sub,* beneath+*cortex,* skin or outer layer.

Situated beneath the cortex. In this book the word refers to inner structures or parts of the brain.

supra- (su prah-) Latin prefix: above.

The suprarenals, for example, are situated above the kidneys. They also are known as the adrenals, from the Latin: *ad,* near *renis,* kidney.

symbiotic (sim bi o tik) Greek: *symbiosis,* living together.

Pertaining to the close association or relationship of two dissimilar organisms or compounds. Psychological meaning pertains to the condition where a characteristic or symptom becomes part of the personality. Children who have felt they are quite retarded are apt to behave as though they really are unintelligent and hopeless. The teacher needs considerable wisdom and ingenuity to fathom such a child and find ways to encourage him.

syndrome (sin drom) Greek: *syndrome,* concurrence.

A set of symptoms that generally occur together. *Gerstmann's* syndrome, for example, includes these signs: finger agnosia, agraphia (difficulty in expressing thoughts in writing), acalculia (difficulty in arithmetic), and left-right confusion. Lesions of the angular gyrus area of the left hemisphere usually bring such symptoms. A somewhat dramatic part of the syndrome that children show with cerebellar injuries or disturbances is the marked tendency to cling to adults for support and attention.

262

synergistic (**sin** er jis tik) Greek: *syn,* together +*ergon,* work.

Acting together to enhance the action or value of each force or agent in the combination. Many drugs are synergistic, exerting far greater effects when acting together than the sum of their separate effects. For children who have felt very jittery and discouraged about themselves, an excellent, imaginative, hopeful teacher plus the right pharmacotherapy—administered by a wise and warmhearted physician and nurse—can be wonderfully synergistic.

thalamus (**thal** ah mus) Greek: *thalamos,* chamber.

The middle and larger portion of the diencephalon, between the hypothalamus and the epithalamus. The thalamus is the main relay center in the brain for sensory impulses coming to cortical areas. Thalamic fibers provide the *circuits* for what we call associative thinking and comprehension. Injury or dysfunction of thalamic tracts can alter a child's ability to think and to behave sensibly.

therapy (**ther** ah pe) Greek: *therapeia,* treatment.

The careful treatment of disease or disorder. In this broad sense, good teaching is therapeutic for children who have felt upset or discouraged. Such teaching, of course, as in all effective medical therapy, has to be based in diagnostic understanding of the child's real troubles. The right treatment, employed early enough to do the most good, is the best therapy in any case.

tonality (ton **al** i te) Greek: *tonos,* tone.

The quality and peculiarity of a tonal system (music, speech, etc.). The *right* hemisphere contains the major areas where tonality is comprehended, though major speech centers are in the *left* hemisphere.

toxicity (toks **is** i te) Greek: *toxikon,* poison.

The quality of being poisonous. Refers especially to the degree of virulence or *pathogenicity* of a substance or microorganism. Many substances and microorganisms that used to be considered harmless have been discovered to be sufficiently toxic to alter or impair brain and nervous tissue.

trauma (**traw** mah) Greek: *trauma,* wound.

Any injury to the body (or mind) caused by violence, as a wound.

Psychic trauma, for example, may result from an emotional shock that makes a profound and lasting impression of the mind. Many children have suffered traumatic experiences.

trophic- (**trof** ik-) Greek: *trophikos,* nourishing.

Of or pertaining to nourishing.

-tropic (**-tro** pik) Greek: *tropikos,* turning.

Pertaining to turning or changing.

vertigo (ver te go) Latin: *vertigo,* a turning around.
Sensation of dizziness, as a whirling motion of oneself or of external objects. May denote cerebral anemia, middle ear disease (as in Meniere's syndrome); may also reflect organic brain or central nervous system disease.

visuo- (viz u o-) Latin: *visus,* seen.
Combining form of visual, pertaining to mental images that are formed partly by visualization. A child's visuoperceptive capacities comprise the main gateways to his early understanding of himself and the world around him.

vulnerability (vul ner ah bil i te) Latin: *vulnerare,* to wound.
Susceptibility to contagion or injury. Some children by nature and early circumstances of their lives are more rugged and sturdy than others, and are able to come through infections or injuries that might hurt more vulnerable youngsters greatly. Children who suffered severe psychic or physical deprivation or injury are apt to be vulnerable to many stresses in life that might not bother other boys or girls at all. Chronic discouragement certainly can make a child more vulnerable to trouble.

xenogenous (zen oj en us) Greek: *xenos,* strange + *gennan,* to produce.
Caused by a foreign substance or body; originating outside the organism.